VIRGINIA ROCKS!

A Guide to Geologic Sites in the Old Dominion

ALBERT B. DICKAS

2019
Mountain Press Publishing Company
Missoula, Montana

Photos by author unless otherwise credited.
Maps constructed by Chelsea Feeney (www.cmcfeeney.com)
Cover photo: Limestone turrets in the Shenandoah Valley at Natural Chimneys Park

Geology Rocks!
A state-by-state series that introduces readers to some of the
most compelling and accessible geologic sites in each state.

 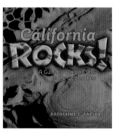    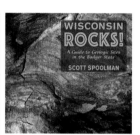

Library of Congress Cataloging-in-Publication Data

Names: Dickas, Albert Binkley, 1933- author.
Title: Virginia rocks! : a guide to geologic sites in the Old Dominion /
  Albert B. Dickas.
Description: Missoula, Montana : Mountain Press Publishing Company, 2019. |
  Series: Geology rocks! | Includes bibliographical references and index.
Identifiers: LCCN 2018046430 | ISBN 9780878426881 (paperback : alk. paper)
Subjects: LCSH: Geology—Virginia—Guidebooks. | Virginia—Guidebooks.
Classification: LCC QE173 .D53 2019 | DDC 557.55—dc23
LC record available at https://lccn.loc.gov/2018046430

PRINTED IN HONG KONG

MP Mountain Press
PUBLISHING COMPANY
P.O. Box 2399 • Missoula, MT 59806 • 406-728-1900
800-234-5308 • info@mtnpress.com
www.mountain-press.com

In memory of my mother,

Helen Binkley Dickas,

who taught me the beauty of words

and their significance in matters

of education and judgment.

PREFACE

Throughout much of the twentieth century, mainstream America was ill-informed regarding the processes and history of that branch of science devoted to the study of Earth. For decades the majority of geologists not engaged in education were employed in explorations for oil, natural gas, coal, or ore deposits—investigations that had long been somewhat static in terms of scientific innovation and informative publicity. Then came change.

The declaration that the worldwide distribution of geologic phenomena, such as mountain building, volcanism, and seismicity, are directly related to the formation, movement, and destruction of a series of rigid, interlocked sections of Earth's crust was initially introduced, in 1912, under the name continental drift, and then rejected. Studies after World War II, however, especially those involving the mysteries of the ocean depths, introduced new and convincing evidence and hypotheses to support a revised version of this theory, repackaged as *plate tectonics*. In the 1960s, the universal acceptance of this theory transformed the way earth scientists think.

In 1970, the celebration of the first Earth Day gave the American public an opportunity to express its concern about the global deterioration of land, water, and atmospheric resources. Overnight the word *environment* became a subject for discussion within a wide range of venues—from the evening news to the halls of government.

As a result of these two watershed declarations—plate tectonics and Earth Day—geology today occupies a leadership role in science, and the public at large is much more informed about the earthly manipulations of Mother Nature, specifically her ability to create beauty and order over the long term and death and destruction in the short term.

Virginia is blessed with a variety of locales closely associated with interesting and educational geologic topics: coal formation, extraterrestrial impact, cavern development, fossil sites, continental bifurcation, volcanic eruption, mountain building, and even a pair of lakes that exhibit decidedly non-lake-like character—one in the middle of a massive swamp and the other atop a mountain peak. All of these topics, and more, are presented herein in text reflective of new-era concepts of geologic understanding and interpretation.

Many of the fifty geologic sites in this travel guide are located on protected, publicly accessible city, state, or federal land. Please do not trespass or collect rock or fossil specimens in restricted areas unless you have obtained permission. For safety reasons, the few rock exposures that are situated along busy highways should be considered drive-by locations only. Finally, keep in mind that many sites operate on a schedule that changes, so it is wise to check websites or call ahead before departure to determine seasons, days, and hours of operation.

I hope your visits to the locales presented in this guide enhance your comprehension of the geologic processes through which they formed, and that you will gain a better understanding of how their presence has defined the topographic profile of the state of Virginia. Perhaps we will run into each other in your meanderings from one site to another. If so, I would be more than pleased to make your acquaintance and autograph your copy of *Virginia Rocks!*

ALBERT BINKLEY DICKAS
Brush Mountain, Virginia
September 2018

ACKNOWLEDGMENTS

The writing of a field guide such as this, highlighting locales of unusual geology and paleontology distributed across ninety-five counties and within the confines of thirty-eight independent cities considered county-equivalents for census purposes, cannot be accomplished in isolation. Many individuals must be involved, and their help, suggestions, and cooperation are hereby gratefully acknowledged.

My editor, James Lainsbury, has been, as always, excessive in patience, generous in encouragement, and thorough in editing. I marvel at his continuing ability to mold a higher degree of consistency and understanding in my use of dates, facts, and concepts.

Published author and valued and cherished friend Rachael M. Garrity, principal of Penworthy LLC, has throughout the writing of this guide tirelessly responded to my frequent and far too often late-hour requests for assistance in matters of grammar, usage, and syntax.

Finally, I would be remiss should I neglect to recognize the many individuals who helped directly and indirectly with the writing of this guide by offering their suggestions and willingness to search out and share information. If listed by name the count would be extensive and I would run the risk of inadvertently overlooking a valued resource, but a mention of the background of those who helped seems in order: personnel with city, county, and governmental parks; reference and resource librarians; mineral, rock, and fossil collectors; university, college, and municipal museum curators; and the staff of numerous city and county historical societies.

I hope I extended a proper sense of appreciation to each of "the many" at the time I visited with them, but if I failed, then here and now I express my heartfelt THANK YOU.

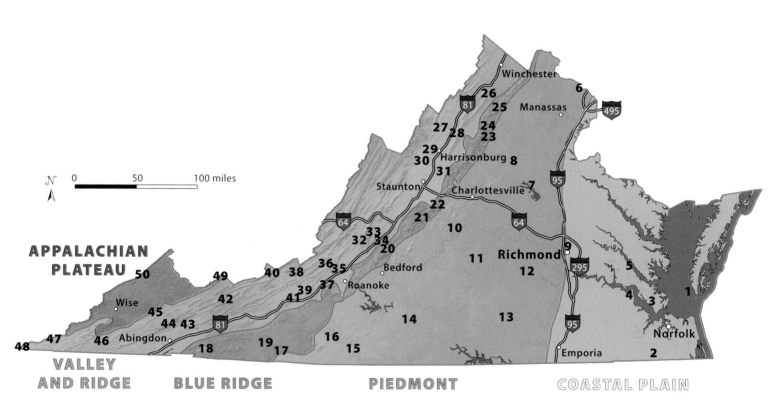

Regions and sites covered in Virginia Rocks! Numbers correspond to the described localities.

CONTENTS

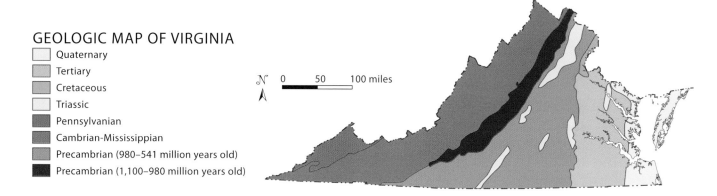

GEOLOGIC MAP OF VIRGINIA

- ☐ Quaternary
- ▨ Tertiary
- ▨ Cretaceous
- ☐ Triassic
- ▨ Pennsylvanian
- ▨ Cambrian-Mississippian
- ▨ Precambrian (980–541 million years old)
- ■ Precambrian (1,100–980 million years old)

N
0 50 100 miles

GEOLOGIC TIMESCALE

Era	Period		Epoch	Age	Notable Geologic Events in Virginia
CENOZOIC	Quaternary		Holocene	0.01	
			Pleistocene	2.6	Pleistocene ice ages
	Tertiary	Neogene	Pliocene	5.3	
			Miocene	23.0	
		Paleogene	Oligocene	33.9	Chesapeake Bay meteorite impact 35 million years ago
			Eocene	56.0	
			Paleocene	66	
MESOZOIC	Cretaceous			145	Breakup of the supercontinent Pangaea 200 million years ago; Triassic basins form; Atlantic Ocean opens up
	Jurassic			201	
	Triassic			252	
PALEOZOIC	Permian			299	Alleghanian Orogeny occurs between 330 and 250 million years ago, finalizes assembly of the Pangaean supercontinent when Africa collides with North America
	Carboniferous		Pennsylvanian	323	Future coal formed from swamps of Pennsylvanian time
			Mississippian	359	
	Devonian			419	Acadian Orogeny occurs between 380 to 340 million years ago
	Silurian			444	
	Ordovician			485	Taconic Orogeny occurs between 460 to 435 million years ago
	Cambrian			541	Cambrian explosion
PRECAMBRIAN	Proterozoic Eon		Neoproterozoic	1,000	Supercontinent Rodinia begins to break up about 730 million years ago
			Mesoproterozoic	1,600	Grenville Orogeny about 1.3 to 1 billion years ago; formation of the supercontinent Rodinia 1.1 billion years ago
			Paleoproterozoic	2,500	
	Archean Eon			3,850	
	Hadean Eon			4,600	approximate age of Earth

Age in millions of years before present

VIRGINIA'S GEOLOGIC HERITAGE
A Chronology of Four Episodes

PRECAMBRIAN TIME
A Long-Ago Beginning

Earth, the third planet from the Sun and the only object in the universe known to harbor life, came into existence approximately 4.54 billion years ago, give or take some 50 million years. This celestial birth date has been determined through the radiometric analyses of hundreds of meteorites collected on all seven continents, and of rocks gathered by American astronauts as they lumbered across the surface of the Moon. Because we can only understand the formation of our planet within the context of the other planets and moons of our solar system, we assume they were created at the same general time, thus the ages of extraterrestrial material can be directly related to the age of Earth.

Recent research suggests the title "oldest rock on Earth" belongs to a gnarled exposure of Nuvvuagittuq greenstone—a form of metamorphosed lava—that has occupied the Hudson Bay area of Canada for at least 4.28 billion years. Older rocks may eventually be found, but in all probability normal geologic processes destroyed them long ago, or they lie at depths in the Earth too great for recovery. In the final analysis, and by any measure of time, one fact stands out with undisputed clarity: Earth is most certainly a senior citizen rock star.

During its early years, Earth was a roiling, boiling sphere of molten rock that was gradually rearranged into three zones. Heavy elements sank to the center to form an iron-rich core, and frothy, low-density material rose to the surface to eventually cool as crust. Material caught in between became the plastic, mushy substance termed *mantle*. A primitive atmosphere enveloped the surface and, as temperatures cooled, moisture-laden clouds condensed to produce the first storms. Oceans filled in low-lying topography, river systems came into being, and the water cycle was born, along with the ever-present processes of weathering and erosion.

Static crustal surfaces became mobile as Rhode Island–sized landmasses crystallized and began to move laterally over Earth's surface, driven by forces that during the mid-1960s were recognized and accepted under the theory of plate tectonics. To understand these forces, it helps to envision a pot of spaghetti sauce simmering on the stovetop. As sauce is heated at the bottom of the pot, it rises, eventually reaching the surface, where it cools and moves laterally to the sides before sinking toward the bottom of the pot again, starting the whole process over. In essence, this is how geoscientists envision that heat moves through the Earth in the form of large, circulating convection currents. Upon reaching the base of Earth's crust, convection currents, in theory, spread laterally, begin to cool, and eventually sink back into the interior, where they are reheated and the entire process begins anew. Upon reaching the basal portions of the crust the currents slowly stretch and break the crust into some twenty large-to-small rigid slabs termed *plates*, which are in continuous motion relative to one another. This process, sometimes called "the dance of the continents," results in three types of interactions: plates pulling apart, plates moving together, and plates grinding past each other. It's important to understand these interactions because they are responsible for much of the amazing phenomena we discuss in geology.

As a result of these ever-moving landmasses, over the course of geologic time protocontinents were born, increased in number, and then coalesced to create the rock-bound interiors of present-day continents. Soon thereafter the entire gamut of geologic process was under way: volcanoes erupted molten rock, earthquakes haphazardly fractured and rearranged Earth's terrestrial architecture, and youthful mountain ranges grew to lofty heights only to bow to the inevitability of erosion, reduced in size to sand and dust.

By middle Precambrian time, 2.5 billion years ago, the dynamic processes of plate tectonics were in full swing. Continents collided, and continents were torn apart; oceans were born, and oceans died; and, at times, all of Earth's continents came together as one major landmass known as a *supercontinent*. It's estimated that this cycle of tectonic change occurred, on average, every 500 million years. Some researchers hypothesize that many supercontinents have existed over geologic time, the oldest being Vaalbara, which supposedly existed 3.6 to 2.8 billion years ago, but evidence regarding most of them are lost in the mists of time. It is generally accepted that two supercontinents formed in the past. The more elderly one, named Rodinia, formed some 1.1 billion years ago when ancestral versions of South America, eastern North America, and western Africa came together as one. The oldest rocks in Virginia formed around this time. Pangaea, the second widely accepted supercontinent, formed much later, during the late Paleozoic Era.

During the early stages of Rodinia's formation, Virginia occupied a coastal position, but 1 billion years ago it collided with a smaller landmass, and the Commonwealth was transferred to an interior location. During the finale of this tectonic fender-bender the Grenville Mountains, a Himalayan-high belt of folded and faulted rock extending from Labrador through Virginia and into Texas, were created.

The biologic curtain rose on a form of single-celled blue-green algae during the Precambrian. It lacked a true nucleus and reproduced the old-fashioned way—asexually. The life cycle of these primitive organisms involved photosynthesis,

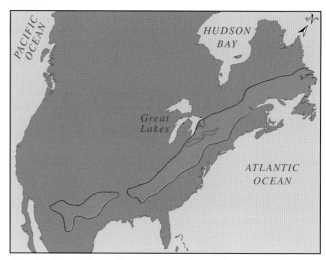

Distribution of Grenville-age rocks (orange) in North America.

which significantly directed Earth's evolution: the toxic, oxygen-starved atmosphere slowly morphed into an inviting environment as these organisms pumped out large volumes of oxygen.

Over time rising oxygen levels gave simple asexual life-forms a choice: move, evolve, or die. Many did expire, but others adapted and evolved to more advanced forms that were larger in size, sported a distinct nucleus, and exchanged genes so that each generation possessed a different genetic configuration and biologic variation. In short, the sexual revolution was underway and Earth began to display its modern complexion.

After the Grenville Mountains had formed, the entire state of Virginia experienced a period of erosion that lasted for hundreds of millions of years. Highland terrain that had once reached beyond the clouds became a landscape of gentle hills and shallow valleys, and eventually even the deep-seated crystalline roots of the Grenville Mountains were exposed to the corrosive effects of wind, water, and gravity. Rodinia began to split apart, and the Iapetus Ocean, considered a precursor of the Atlantic Ocean, began developing off the east coast of North America.

Today the ancient rocks of the Grenville Mountains form the basement of Virginia. Geoscientists have used an array of geophysical methods to develop a broad understanding of the physical makeup and depth of these rocks. These rock analyses indicate that igneous and metamorphic rocks constitute the bulk of the Blue Ridge Mountains and are distributed throughout the Piedmont Province, Virginia's largest physiographic province. Lying between the Fall Line, the line of East Coast rapids and waterfalls that formed where rivers cross from hard bedrock to softer sediments, and the Blue Ridge Province, the Piedmont is characterized by gently undulating topography, heavily weathered bedrock, and a general absence of solid outcrop.

Approximately 570 million years ago fissure eruptions, ejections of volcanic material from elongate fractures rather than central vents, began to vomit lava onto the surface of Virginia. Continuing for 20 million years, these eruptions covered large sections of the Blue Ridge region with basalt—7,200 cubic miles in total—of the Catoctin Formation. Metamorphism later altered the basalt to greenstone, so named for the greenish tint caused by chlorite and epidote minerals.

As the Precambrian came to an end, the terrain of the Commonwealth could best be described as geologically complex and topographically simple. A very long period of time involving planetary birth, tectonic growth and destruction, biologic evolution, and topographic development had run its course, and the stage was set for the next chapter of Earth history.

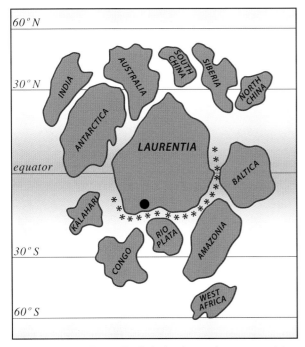

The supercontinent Rodinia in the early stages of its breakup approximately 730 million years ago. The Iapetus Ocean (identified by the line of asterisks) developed between Laurentia (early North America) and Amazonia (central South America), Rio Plata (southern South America), and Baltica (northwestern Eurasia). Present-day Virginia is represented by the black circle in the southern portion of Laurentia.

PALEOZOIC ERA
Appalachian Evolution and Biologic Progress

Cambrian Period

At the start of the Cambrian Period, 541 million years ago, the Sun rose on a world in disarray. Rodinia continued to break into a cluster of smaller landmasses, or protocontinents, separated from each other by an ever-widening Iapetus Ocean—the predecessor of the present-day Atlantic Ocean. Spreading at a speed comparable to the growth of the human fingernail, the dividing plates engaged in a slow tectonic dance that affected the atmosphere, altered oceanic circulation patterns, and created environments conducive to the evolution of marine plants and animals.

Virginia was positioned south of the equator, bathed in a tropical climate with the rest of Laurentia, ancestor of today's North America. Terrestrial vegetation was nonexistent, and the lack of a protective organic soil gave rise to a deeply furrowed landscape. Over time the Iapetus Ocean rose. Its shoreline advanced westward over Virginia, and rivers draining off the eroded flanks of the Grenville Mountains deposited expansive layers of sand and mud across the continental shelf. Compressed into sandstone and shale, this thickening pile of sedimentary rock, along with layers of limestone deposited in the open ocean, buried the Catoctin Formation basalt to depths of thousands of feet.

A wide variety of large, multicellular life-forms appeared abruptly on the evolutionary scene in what's known as the "Cambrian explosion," an event unique to the annals of geologic history. A rich and varied suite of marine life developed, but most phyla were represented by only a few species. This exclusive aquatic community consisted principally of brachiopods, corals, sponges, and trilobites, mobile millimeter-to-foot-long creatures that filtered food from mud and silt deposits covering the seafloor. Trilobites made up about half of the biomass in the Iapetus Ocean and, by the very nature of their numbers, occupied a position near the top of the food chain. By late Cambrian time, however, they reached their peak in dominance and then gradually declined in number.

As Cambrian time drew to an end, Laurentia remained tectonically stable. Erosion was the dominant force affecting the landscape. Virginia was evolving into an array of denuded hills and valleys silhouetted to the northwest by the now all but invisible remains of the once lofty Grenville Mountains. Over the course of 56 million years, great change had taken place, perhaps the most important of which was the development of exoskeletons. Moving forward this mineralized armor would protect marine organisms from a host of dangers: ultraviolet radiation, predators, and death by dehydration in fluctuating, shallow-water environments.

Ordovician Period

Throughout the Ordovician Period, 485 to 444 million years ago, plate tectonic forces incrementally rotated Laurentia in a counterclockwise direction, moving the future Commonwealth ever closer to the equator and into a warmer environment. A universal rise in sea level introduced the Tippecanoe Sea, an extensive, shallow body of saltwater that extended from the Arctic islands south and west to Mexico.

This warm body of water, today recognized as the greatest inundation of a continental landmass in the entirety of geologic history, completely submerged Virginia.

Off the east coast of submerged Laurentia subterranean pods of molten magma migrated to the surface, adding fuel to an arc of volcanic islands that had been created by subduction. *Subduction* is the process by which one tectonic plate descends into the Earth beneath another, where it heats up and melts, becoming the source of newly generated magma. Rising to heights in excess of 12,000 feet and stretching for some 2,000 miles, the curved, linear belt of volcanic islands off the coast of Laurentia was the sole body of land interrupting the surface of the Iapetus Ocean.

Great volumes of lava and ash were erupted across and within the ocean as the volcanic arc inched its way toward Laurentia, pulled ever closer toward the subduction zone. It eventually fused to the edge of Laurentia. This head-on collision of terranes is called the Taconic Orogeny—an event of folding, faulting, and metamorphism that constitutes the first of three phases of mountain building that formed the Appalachian Mountains during the Paleozoic Era. This orogeny resulted in the Taconic Mountains, a chain of volcanoes composed of a complex mass of igneous rock. With heights that rivaled those of the modern Rocky Mountains, these highlands extended from northern Maine southwest to the northern reaches of Georgia. The Taconic Mountains that form the New York border with Vermont, Massachusetts, and Connecticut are their deeply eroded remnants.

Surface-feeding organisms replaced bottom-feeders, and a diverse population of bryozoans and corals built relatively small patch reefs that gave character to the otherwise nondescript seafloor that was Virginia. The tepid, oxygenated sea created a utopia that became home to more than five hundred families of marine organisms. Clusters of bryozoans (moss animals) were the most abundant, followed by scatterings of solitary brachiopods (lampshells). Pelecypods (clams), cephalopods (squid), and gastropods (snails), all 1 inch or so in size, abounded, but trilobite species declined in number, continuing a trend that had begun during Cambrian time.

Mud was the principal deposit in the deeper waters off-shore of Laurentia, while soupy and slimy ooze, composed of as much as 90 percent calcareous skeletal material, collected in shallower areas in the interior of the continent. The latter was eventually compressed into limestone. Within the confines of the Shenandoah Valley this limestone today is riddled with caverns due to dissolution, the process whereby acidic groundwater dissolves calcareous bedrock. This unusual subterranean environment, stretching from the latitude of Winchester southward to Roanoke, fuels a flourishing tourism economy centered on the splendors of stalactite- and stalagmite-laden chambers.

The end of Ordovician time was marked by the extinction of many groups of marine organisms, especially bryozoans and brachiopods. Researchers believe this extinction event, one of five such major events in Earth's history, was the result of glaciation centered at the South Pole. Sea levels dropped as water took the form of glaciers, and as much as 60 percent of marine life went extinct as a result.

Silurian Period

During the Silurian Period, 444 to 419 million years ago, a tranquil environment developed across the length and breadth of Laurentia. The climate was balmy and arid, the once towering Taconic Mountains in central Virginia had been reduced to a peneplain—a low-relief, nearly featureless and gently undulating land surface of considerable area—and waters of the Tippecanoe Sea had filled in the lowlands lying west of the eroded highlands, extending into what is now West Virginia and beyond.

Limestone deposition dominated the coastal regions of the Tippecanoe Basin, accompanied by an explosive growth of patch reefs, layered ridgelike structures built by sedentary calcareous organisms, most commonly colonial corals. In deeper waters offshore of Laurentia, high evaporation rates created conditions conducive to the precipitation of layers of halite and anhydrite hundreds of feet thick, such as the historic exposures in the Saltville region of southwestern Virginia.

Life in the Tippecanoe Sea remained relatively unchanged from that of Ordovician time, but several new species evolved and became a lethal threat to anything that moved. Paramount among these predators were the acanthodians, the first fish with jaws. Characterized by large eyes, a strong bite, and body-covering spines, the earliest of these organisms were exclusively marine, but later versions evolved to inhabit freshwater environments. The family of acanthodians included the first true sharks, with skeletons composed of cartilage, organic tissue that is softer and more flexible than bone.

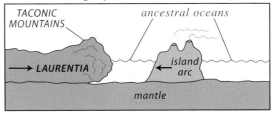

A. Taconic Orogeny (460–435 million years ago)

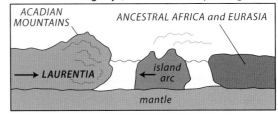

B. Acadian Orogeny (380–340 million years ago)

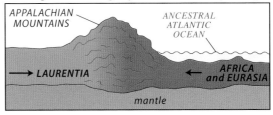

C. Alleghanian Orogeny (330–250 million years ago)

The Appalachian Mountains, created over a span of some 200 million years by the collision of various landmasses during three different orogenies, cross Virginia in the form of three physiographic provinces: Blue Ridge, Valley and Ridge, and Appalachian Plateau.

During the Silurian, simple vascular plants were in an early stage of development and altered the raw nature of the land to conditions verdant, earthy, and fertile. With landscapes covered by a blanket of organic softness, rainfall was more easily absorbed as groundwater, thereby reducing the volume of surface runoff and the effects of erosion on the landscape. Virginia, along with the majority of Laurentia, was still inundated by the Tippecanoe Sea.

As the Sun set on the Silurian Period, the shoreline of the Tippecanoe Sea began to move to the south of Virginia as compressional forces began to uplift portions of eastern Laurentia. This retreat left in its wake a blanket of pure quartz sand, which eventually lithified as sandstone filled with a rich catalog of brachiopod fossils. Today this stone is a valuable raw material used in the manufacture of a variety of glass products. Soon all of Virginia was high and dry, and the rumblings of tectonic activity heralded a new episode of mountain building. The microcontinent of Avalonia, one of the smaller landmasses created by the breakup of Rodinia, was migrating westward, soon to make scraping and grinding contact with Laurentia. This event, termed the Acadian Orogeny, was the second of three intense periods of regional deformation that crafted the Appalachian Mountains.

Devonian Period

Dense sulfur-bearing clouds rolled across Virginia as a new generation of magma chambers were activated beneath the eroded roots of the Taconic Mountains. Multiple series of volcanoes erupted during the Devonian, 419 to 359 million years ago, and earthquakes fractured the land with increased frequency and intensity as the Acadian Mountains grew and the southern Iapetus Ocean closed.

Born when ancestral Eurasia, one of the landmasses created when Rodinia broke up at the end of the Precambrian, collided with the east coast of Laurentia, the Acadian Mountains eventually extended northward from Florida to the Canadian Maritime Provinces. Rivers draining their western flank deposited thick sequences of organic-rich sediment that are exposed today as folded and faulted packages of sedimentary rock throughout the Valley and Ridge and Appalachian Plateau Provinces. These wedges of sandstone and shale grow thinner toward the west because the farther the rivers were from the mountain sources of sediment, the less sediment they carried and subsequently deposited. Geologists catalog these rocks as a delta complex, a fan-shaped plain composed of two or more deltas.

Imagine the Acadians hundreds of millions of years ago, with wedge-shaped piles of sediment draped along the range's western flank and terminating in the shrinking Iapetus Ocean. The older of the two wedges, called the Catskill delta, decreases in thickness, from 8,500 feet near Winchester to 1,000 feet in far southwest Virginia, and the younger Pocono sequence decreases from 1,700 feet near Blacksburg to 150 feet in the vicinity of the Virginia-Tennessee border.

Virginia's Devonian strata rival its Ordovician rocks in terms of fossil abundance and diversity. Brachiopods, corals, bryozoans, and some trilobites are widely distributed. Analyses of microscopic growth-ring patterns ornamenting the surface of rugose corals indicate the Devonian calendar had 410 days a year, a reduction of 20 days over the prior 100 million years. This indicates that the rotational velocity of Earth was declining, so a typical Devonian day in the Commonwealth lasted some 21.6 hours compared to 20.7 hours during the Cambrian Period. Tidal "braking," friction created by the interactions between Earth and its moon and the daily rise and fall of ocean tides, has caused Earth to slow even more, giving us the 24-hour day, of which there are 365 in a year. In short, the Earth day will continue to be lengthened by 0.002 seconds per century for the foreseeable future.

In contrast to the tropical conditions of the Silurian Period, Virginia was now situated in a humid equatorial belt crossed by moisture-laden wind blowing out of the east, relative to today's continental configurations. Clouds rose as they approached the Acadian Mountains and dumped massive volumes of rain that nourished primitive generations of groundcover shrubs and plants, flora that possessed seeds, true roots, leaves, and massive limbs that grew to treelike form. Earth's green revolution was evolving.

Then, some 360 million years ago, surface ocean temperatures plummeted by as much as 15 degrees Fahrenheit, and 70 percent of warm-water invertebrate species went extinct. Reef communities were severely impacted, as were graptolites, small colonial animals with a fingernail-like outer covering, and cystoids, plantlike animals that lived attached to the seafloor by stalks. Trilobites developed smaller eyes, perhaps in response to increasing levels of turbidity in the oceans. The first tetrapods, however, filled the evolutionary void. These early amphibians had four leglike structures and are believed to have inhabited coastal and brackish marine environments, waiting for food to be washed ashore by tidal and storm waves. They are representative of fauna undergoing a transition from life in the sea to life on land.

Popular theories regarding the cause of the Devonian extinction event include bolide impact and widespread eruptions of lava, both of which could have affected the atmosphere by reducing the amount of sunlight reaching Earth's surface. The "Devonian plant hypothesis," first proposed in 1995, suggests that the expansion of terrestrial plants was a prime cause for the Devonian extinction event. Their spread could have resulted in greater amounts of organic matter in the oceans, which could have deprived bottom waters of oxygen—a process called eutrophication—and killed marine life.

Mississippian Period

From its somewhat benign beginning 359 million years ago to its threatening end, the Mississippian Period lasted 36 million years. Throughout most of the world strata of this age are indistinguishable from those of the Pennsylvanian Period, thus the two time periods are commonly lumped together and called the Carboniferous. In the United States, however, Carboniferous-age rocks are easy to differentiate. Therefore they are conventionally divided into the older Mississippian and younger Pennsylvanian systems on the basis of, respectively, the relative absence or presence of coal.

The Mississippian was an unusual time of transition, with change taking place both biologically and geologically. Life, on the path to recovery from the dark days associated with the Devonian extinction event, began to branch out in new directions. Representatives of several plant and animal groups are found in unimaginable numbers in Mississippian strata. Blastoids, crinoids, and lacy bryozoans are of primary importance in the fossil record because they are useful in determining the relative age of their host rock. One formation in Kentucky is reported to contain up to 300 quadrillion crinoid fossils, a figure that supports the name that has long been given to the Mississippian Period: Age of Crinoids.

Topographically Virginia once again assumed a low profile. The Acadian Mountains had been worn down to nubs. From Virginia's western boundary eastward to beyond the longitude of Richmond the lay of the land is best described as a peneplain, an advanced stage of erosion that had last occurred in the state during the Silurian Period. Three suites of sedimentary rock were deposited across this peneplain: lower units dominated by clastic sediment, a middle carbonate sequence, and upper units of fine-grained sediment that are evidence of developing tectonic activity. The middle sequence, highlighted by the Greenbrier Limestone, is evidence of a warm, shallow, clear, and highly agitated sea characterized by an abundance of invertebrate life. Known as the Kaskaskia Sea, this inland body of water stretched all the way from Pennsylvania and Virginia westward to Nevada.

Oolites are a characteristic feature of Mississippian-age carbonate rocks in Virginia. These miniature spheres are composed of concentric layers of calcium carbonate that formed around a nucleus, such as a shell fragment. Typically smaller than 0.08 inch in diameter, they can be found in present-day warm-water areas, such as the Bahamas and the Arabian Gulf. Their presence in an ancient rock indicates the rock was deposited in fair-to-warm-weather conditions and at a shallow depth—shallow enough for the waves to be able to reach down and gently stir these growing "carbonate hailstones," coating them evenly with calcium carbonate.

Ice sheets waxed and waned across the southern hemisphere, and the average global temperature hovered around a moderate 54 degrees Fahrenheit. All across Laurentia life took advantage of this relatively mild climate, and the biologic spotlight began to focus more on the evolution of terrestrial flora than changes in the quality and quantity of marine fauna. Forests were adding both a canopy of shade and a degree of future economic value (think coal) to the complexion of Earth.

The future seemed like it might be uneventful. However, east of Laurentia a mountain-building event that would rival the intensity of the Grenville Orogeny was underway. Its tectonic consequence would elevate the Appalachian Mountains to excessive heights and a mature status.

Pennsylvanian Period

Early on during the Pennsylvanian Period, which lasted from 323 to 299 million years ago, migrating ancestral continents—northwest Africa and portions of Europe—collided with the eastern seaboard of Laurentia and significantly changed the face of Virginia. This mountain-building event, known as the Alleghanian Orogeny, was the last major orogeny to affect the Mid-Atlantic region. It took place during the early stages of construction of the supercontinent Pangaea. Virginia had already been geologically restructured by three orogenies, the Grenville having formed mountains of the same name during Precambrian time, and the Taconic and the Acadian that had occurred earlier in Paleozoic time. With the Alleghanian virtually the entire state became mountainous, and the heights of the range rivaled the present-day Himalayan Mountains.

Across the entirety of the Commonwealth rocks were compressed, folded, faulted, and moved great distances from their original locations. Rhode Island–sized terranes were literally caught between a rock and a hard place. For example, one massive slab of igneous and metamorphic material was thrust up and over one composed of younger sedimentary strata, forming a stacked and overlapping sequence of rocks resembling overlapping shingles on a roof. Through this process of compression the lateral extent of Virginia was being reduced and the Appalachian Mountains were being pushed upward to their full topographic glory.

In the southern hemisphere glaciers expanded and contracted, causing worldwide variations in sea level, while in Virginia turbid rivers flowing west off the mountains transported and deposited huge volumes of sediment that were later compacted into various types of sedimentary rock. Beyond the western mountain front the land looked like the present-day Atchafalaya Swamp of Louisiana and the Everglades of Florida. Environments characterized by sluggish streams, lakes, marshes, and stagnant lagoons dominated a landscape blanketed with ferns, reeds, and horsetail rushes, and the canopies of scale trees exceeded heights of 100 feet. Buried, compressed, and heated, this vegetation is today cataloged as the seventy-six discrete beds of bituminous, subbituminous, and anthracite coal that constitute the "black gold" inventory of Virginia.

The boggy nature of the lowlands encouraged two major innovations: the durable, shelled amniotic egg, which allowed the transition from an aquatic to a terrestrial environment by permitting eggs to be laid away from standing water, and coniferous trees, which preferred higher and drier ground. As a result, plant and animal life was no longer dependent on an aquatic environment for reproduction. New types of amphibians—some snake-like and others salamander-like—arrived, followed by the earliest reptiles. After the Alleghanian Orogeny North America would never again experience the periodic inundations of seawater that had dominated the previous 250 million years. From here on out, North America and the Commonwealth would remain dry.

Permian Period

The Permian Period, spanning from 299 to 252 million years ago, demarcates the end of the Paleozoic Era. The tectonic crescendo known as the Alleghanian Orogeny raised the Appalachian Mountains to unimaginable elevations while, simultaneously, the greatest mass extinction event recorded so far nearly terminated most of Earth's life-forms.

For the first time since Rodinia had coalesced more than 700 million years earlier, a new supercontinent had been assembled. Shaped like the letter C, Pangaea, meaning "one Earth," extended from pole to pole. Virginia was located near its center, with the Panthalassa Ocean to the west and the Tethys Ocean to the east. The Appalachian Mountains delineated the suture along which ancestral Europe and Africa had collided with Laurentia.

Permian-age strata are rare in Virginia, and those rocks that do exist are not particularly fossiliferous. A few reptile and amphibian bones, freshwater invertebrates, and plant and

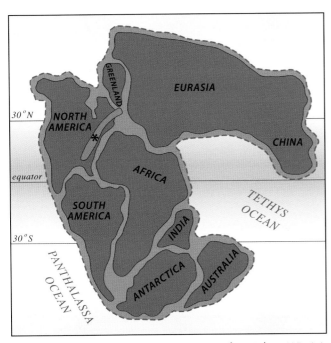

The position of the Appalachian Mountains (purple) and Virginia (asterisk) on the supercontinent Pangaea (dashed line) during the late Paleozoic and early Mesozoic Eras.

Scientists are still debating the cause of this extinction calamity. Did an extraterrestrial body collide with Earth, causing worldwide ecological change, or was the culprit widespread volcanism that released immense clouds of ash that, in turn, sullied the clear-water environments of the oceans? Perhaps the great mass of Pangaea disrupted ocean currents, causing the water to grow stagnant and creating bog-like conditions in the oceans' depths. Climate change and carbon dioxide buildup might also have been factors. Regardless of which theory is correct, without doubt the final assembly of all landmasses during the Permian Period was nearly fatal to the one characteristic that makes Earth unique in its solar system: life.

MESOZOIC ERA
The Fracturing of Virginia

For hundreds of millions of years leading up to the Mesozoic Era, the Commonwealth had been periodically affected by the invasion and retreat of epicontinental seas—large, shallow seas that cover inland portions of a continent. But now Virginia was positioned above sea level, so the inverse became true. Whereas before, rock construction and sedimentation were the primary processes shaping the state, now the destructive forces of wind, running water, and gravity took over. This shift in function is clear in Virginia's Mesozoic Era rock record. Except for one significant example—clastic strata within rift structures—the absence rather than the presence of sedimentary rock characterizes this era.

During the Triassic Period, 252 to 201 million years ago, Pangaea reached senior-citizen status, and the deep-seated tectonic forces that had assembled this supercontinent began to tear it apart. From the northern shores of Labrador to the offshore waters of Florida, this one-Earth colossus started to rift—and ruptured to form the northern hemisphere continents of Europe and North America, separated by the Atlantic Ocean. The primary zone of faulting along which Pangaea fragmented is today recognized as the Mid-Atlantic Ridge, a plate boundary located along the floor of the Atlantic

insect parts have been discovered, but the record is sparse and incomplete. This paucity of fossils is directly related to the clarifying incident—the Permian extinction event, also known as "the great dying"—that marked the end of both the Permian Period and the Paleozoic Era. Within a short span of perhaps 60,000 years, 95 percent of all marine species and 70 percent of their terrestrial brethren became extinct. Trilobites ceased to exist, bryozoans were decimated, and only one family of crinoids survived. Organisms with calcium carbonate exoskeletons were primarily affected because increased ocean acidity, caused by increased atmospheric carbon dioxide, caused them to weaken or not form properly in the first place. Earth came close to becoming biologically barren as life teetered on the brink of oblivion.

Ocean, though a small section crosses a broken terrain of volcanic rock on Iceland.

In spite of the general lack of sedimentary rock, evidence of this division can be seen in the red-rock strata exposed in several Triassic-age rift basins that outcrop across Virginia: Culpeper to the north, centered in Prince William County; Richmond, around the city of Richmond; and the Danville to the south, centered on the community of Chatham in Pittsylvania County. Typically half graben in construction (a valley faulted on one side but not the other), rift basins are conventionally filled with terrestrial gravel, sand, and silt intermixed with freshwater lake deposits. Reptile footprints, often preserved in amazing detail, including those of early dinosaurs, can be found crisscrossing mudflat shale and meandering river sandstone strata. Compared to the C-section incision that is the Mid-Atlantic Ridge, these rift basins are "geologic stretch marks," so to speak, secondary zones of faulting that serve as visible onshore evidence of the gargantuan forces that killed Pangaea and gave birth to the Atlantic Ocean.

During the remaining stretch of the Mesozoic, composed of the Jurassic and Cretaceous Periods (201 to 66 million years ago), the geologic environment of Virginia can be defined as calm and quiet. The long history of earthquakes, mountain building, and volcanism that formed the core of modern-day Virginia had come to an end, and erosion, the mechanical and chemical destruction of the land, became the dominant force.

CENOZOIC ERA
The Modern World Emerges

During the 66 million years that define the Cenozoic Era, the topographic profile of Virginia was continually being altered by the forces of nature, principally wind, water, gravity, and deposition, until the contemporary lay of the land emerged in the form of the state's five physiographic provinces: the Coastal Plain, Piedmont, Blue Ridge, Valley and Ridge, and Appalachian Plateau.

During the Pleistocene Epoch, 2.6 million to 10,000 years ago, continental-sized glaciers, or ice sheets, centered on the Hudson Bay region of Canada expanded outward in all directions, reaching as far south as the latitude of the Ohio River. More than 1 mile thick, they never reached the Commonwealth but were responsible for the frigid periglacial conditions—climate influenced by the cold temperatures beyond the ice front—that enveloped Virginia throughout the Pleistocene. The freeze-thaw action of long winters and strong winds reduced many mountaintop elevations to disarrayed accumulations of angular blocks of bedrock.

Tusks, teeth, and bones of a variety of Pleistocene fauna—mastodons, dire wolves, saber-toothed cats, ground sloths, and even gargantuan 10-foot-tall, 10-ton woolly mammoths—tell the tale of an extinction event that punctuated this extended winter. Whether these animals went extinct due to climate change, overhunting by early human populations, a combination of the two, or something else entirely, we may never know. We do know, however, that the ice sheets and glaciers retreated at the end of the Pleistocene. Today, the remnants of these North American ice sheets are found throughout the Canadian Arctic and covering Greenland with a maximum ice thickness of 2 miles. They are being reduced in size and shape at an alarming rate due to the effects of global warming.

The shrinking ice sheets and many other narratives are part of the geologic history that continues to write itself. For example, in the early afternoon of August 23, 2011, an earthquake ruptured the northern Piedmont Province. Centered midway between Richmond and Charlottesville, 5 miles southwest of the small town of Mineral, it was not a killer quake, but its magnitude rating of 5.8 qualified it to be the strongest tremor recorded on the East Coast in nearly seven decades. Felt across more than a dozen US states and several Canadian provinces, the tectonic rumblings lasted less than one minute, resulted in some $250 million in damage, and caused the general public to drop its assumption that Virginia is free of the seismic forces that ravage the Western states, especially California.

The event occurred within the confines of the Virginia Seismic Zone, a 3,000-square-mile region of historic earthquake activity centered on Goochland County. Because this area and the entire state of Virginia are situated near the middle of the North American tectonic plate, they should, strictly speaking, be free of such activity. Plate tectonic theory posits that earthquakes generally occur along the edges of tectonic plates—those regions where the plates are either colliding or breaking apart—and not within them. Theory is not fact, of course, and this 2011 event is evidence that the forces that created Virginia, while largely recorded in the pages of geologic history, are still capable of now and then rearranging the topographic profile of the Commonwealth.

EPILOGUE

Over the past two centuries, generations of scientists have determined the geologic history of Virginia by scouring the countryside and delving into every nook and cranny where rock could be found. In spite of this history of extensive exploration the record is incomplete. Because Virginia's rock record begins around 1.2 billion years ago, approximately 3.4 billion years of Precambrian history is unknown, and significant exposures of rock representing younger time periods are yet to be found, if they exist at all. The sum of these missing time segments—Precambrian time plus 135 million years of the Jurassic and Cretaceous Periods of the Mesozoic Era and 63 million years of the Tertiary Period of the Cenozoic Era—is some 3.6 billion years, or 78 percent of the 4.6-billion-year age of Earth. The record of the geologic history of the Commonwealth is, therefore, like a 100-page book that contains 22 pages of informative text intermixed with 78 blank pages.

Nevertheless, geoscientists have determined much of the Commonwealth's deep-time history. Virginia was born when ancient continents crystallized and then merged as larger landmasses; it progressed through youthfulness when life evolved in the oceans and then moved onto land, and the Appalachian Mountains gained stature; and it matured when the cold winds of the Pleistocene scoured the landscape.

The study of geology is largely guided by the concept that the present is the key to the past. Turning this statement inside out—the past is the key to the future—gives credence to the prediction that the ever-present geologic forces of construction and destruction will continue to affect Virginia into the distant future.

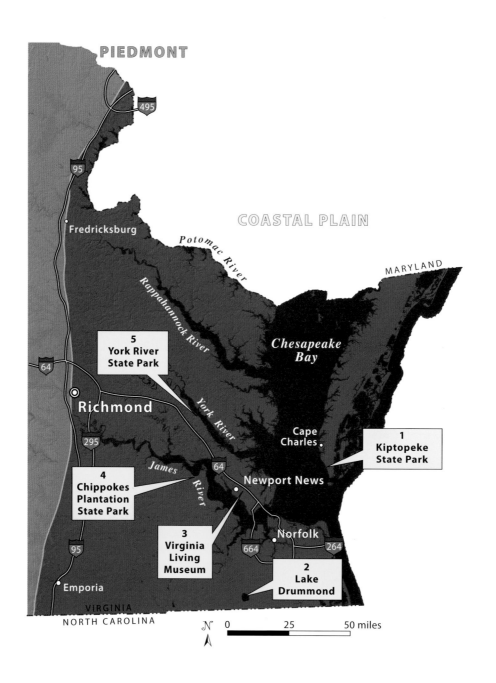

PIEDMONT

COASTAL PLAIN

MARYLAND

Potomac River

Fredricksburg

Rappahannock River

Chesapeake
Bay

5
York River
State Park

Richmond

York River

Cape
Charles

1
Kiptopeke
State Park

James
River

64

Newport News

4
Chippokes
Plantation
State Park

3
Virginia
Living
Museum

Norfolk

664

264

2
Lake
Drummond

Emporia

VIRGINIA
NORTH CAROLINA

0   25   50 miles

COASTAL PLAIN

Low, flat, and incised by three major rivers—the James, York, and Rappahannock—the Coastal Plain Province, also known as the Tidewater region, stretches from the Fall Line east to the low-tide stage of the Atlantic Ocean. Included within its margins is the Eastern Shore, the two-county (Accomack and Northampton) peninsula that is separated from the mainland by the Chesapeake Bay. The Coastal Plain landscape is terraced toward the coast along a series of "steps and treads," the "steps" interpreted as the sites of ancient shorelines, and the "treads" as bays and river bottoms that developed after ocean levels dropped. Distinctive in profile, this landscape formed over a multimillion-year period as sea level ebbed and rose in response to the repeated growth and melting of Pleistocene-age glaciers.

Resembling a wedge of semiconsolidated sediment in cross section, the Coastal Plain is feather-thin inland and increases to more than 10,000 feet offshore. The geology of this region can be presented simply as an undisturbed column of Cenozoic-age strata lacking any signs of mountain building or other tectonic catastrophe. The sole exception to this mental image of deep-time serenity is a buried 50-mile-wide crater that formed 35 million years ago, when a bolide smashed into the east coast of Virginia. Known as the Chesapeake Bay Impact Crater, it is one of the largest impact craters known on Earth.

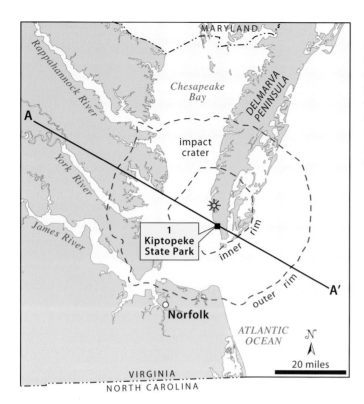

Location of the inner and outer rims of the buried crater (denoted by dashed lines) created by the bolide pressure wave that impacted the eastern seaboard 35 million years ago. The star shows the bull's-eye of the Chesapeake Bay crater, and the line (A–A') corresponds to the cross section.

1 KIPTOPEKE STATE PARK
Chesapeake Bay Impact Crater
37° 10' 01" North, 75° 59' 17" West

Visitors to Kiptopeke State Park, in Northampton County, are uncommonly rich in praise in regard to its setting: stupendous, beautiful, spectacular, and, of course, awesome. A wordsmith might easily group these comments under the heading *serene*. If those same visitors could travel back in time 35 million years, however, their perceptions of the same countryside would most certainly be different—explosive, destructive, and incinerating. The same wordsmith would certainly categorize these unsettling and disturbing descriptions as *cataclysmic*.

At that time tropical rainforests cast deep shadows across the Appalachian Mountains, the Atlantic Ocean shoreline

extended inland to present-day Richmond, dinosaurs had been extinct for 30 million years, and the advent of hominids lay 30 million years down the road. The future site of Kiptopeke State Park lay beneath hundreds of feet of water. *Serene* might have been an apt description for this locale on most days during the Eocene Epoch, except on this one day that the sky took on a strange appearance.

Traveling 70,000 miles per hour, a 15,000-foot-wide bolide careened toward Earth. Vaporizing before impact, its shock wave ripped a hole in the ocean floor 50 miles across and 1 mile deep. Millions of tons of rock debris exploded upward, traveling 30 miles into the atmosphere. Every living thing—plant and animal—for hundreds of miles was instantly reduced to ash, and tsunami waves crashed against the foothills of the Blue Ridge Mountains.

Standing on the beach at Kiptopeke State Park, it is hard to believe that ground zero of this history-altering, Earth-shattering event lies a mere 7 miles to the north. Although park property geographically lies well within the boundary of the impact zone, geologic evidence is buried at a depth of several thousand feet. A core drilled in 1983 by shipboard scientists conducting routine seafloor investigations offshore Atlantic City contained layers of impact breccia, a type of coarse-grained clastic rock associated with documented impact sites. Additional cores retrieved during a follow-up drilling program contained tektites, or pitted beads of fused glass, and shocked quartz displaying parallel fractures, all bona fide signatures of an extraterrestrial impact event. Today such an occurrence would most certainly spell the end for millions of individuals, as well as the destruction of a significant portion of the infrastructure of the eastern seaboard.

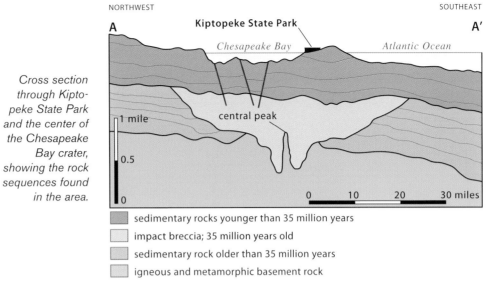

NORTHWEST   SOUTHEAST

A   A'

Kiptopeke State Park

Chesapeake Bay   *Atlantic Ocean*

central peak

1 mile

0.5

0

0   10   20   30 miles

Cross section through Kipto-peke State Park and the center of the Chesapeake Bay crater, showing the rock sequences found in the area.

███ sedimentary rocks younger than 35 million years

░░░ impact breccia; 35 million years old

▒▒▒ sedimentary rock older than 35 million years

░░░ igneous and metamorphic basement rock

The tranquil present-day shoreline at Kiptopeke State Park. The bolide struck just beyond the horizon (left center), creating a topographic depression that ultimately influenced the location and shape of Chesapeake Bay.

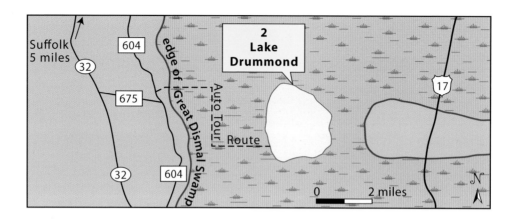

LAKE DRUMMOND
A Fire Scar in the Great Dismal Swamp?
36° 35′ 29″ North, 76° 29′ 17″ West

No two bodies of inland water are the same. They differ in size, depth, and, more importantly, origin. Those in Minnesota—the Land of 10,000 Lakes—formed when glaciers that once covered the state melted. Great Salt Lake exists because it formed in a basin that has no outlet. Many Florida lakes occupy sinkhole depressions that pockmark the state's limestone bedrock. In Virginia, however, there are only two natural lakes, and historically the origins of both have been shrouded in controversy. Consensus seems to have been reached for Mountain Lake (see site 38), but experts continue to debate the origins of Lake Drummond.

Nearly circular in shape and only 6 feet deep, Lake Drummond has maintained its gravity-defying location for thousands of years. It rests at the highest surveyed point in the Great Dismal Swamp, the vast, marshy terrain that covers the Coastal Plain of southeastern Virginia. Since no rivers flow into Lake Drummond, its very existence seems problematic from hydrologic and geographic perspectives.

Climate-change theorists suggest the lake formed naturally, comparable to how contemporary lakes formed on the Arctic Coastal Plain following the retreat of Pleistocene-age glaciers. Naysayers contend that such an origin would have obviously created many low-lying lakes, not just a single one perched on a hill, and they emphasize that Virginia wasn't covered by Pleistocene glaciers. Alternatively, space scientists view the shoreline outline as being the result of meteorite impact, but the absence of collaborating evidence, such as meteorite fragments and shocked quartz, dooms this idea.

Fire sparked by a lightning strike, however, could have burned down through the highly flammable surface layer of peat to the dense clay layer that prevents water from draining into underlying sand. Such a conflagration could result in a bowl-shaped depression that would eventually fill with rainwater. The fact that lighting is attracted to elevated locales suggests that a fire-and-rainwater theory may be the best explanation for Lake Drummond.

Quaternary-age peat (black layer) forms the organic foundation of the Great Dismal Swamp and may have been key to the formation of Lake Drummond.

Lake Drummond, viewed from the observation pier at the end of the 6-mile-long Railroad Ditch Road. Shallow, semicircular, and 3,100 acres in size, the origin of this body of freshwater remains controversial.

VIRGINIA LIVING MUSEUM
Deep-Time Terror along the Dinosaur Discovery Trail
37° 04' 12" North, 76° 28' 49" West

Sometime around 240 million years ago a diverse assemblage of reptiles assumed an alpha position among Earth's vertebrate life. Over the course of the next 175 million years more than one thousand different species evolved, some munching their way through life as vegetarians while others adopted cannibalistic habits. Ranging from 20 inches to 130 feet long and weighing as much as 80 tons, they seemed destined to rule forever. Then, 66 million years ago, their reign of terror ended in the geologic blink of an eye. Dinosaurs are gone, to be sure, but fortunately they have not been forgotten.

In the autumn of 2016 the Virginia Living Museum, in Newport News, opened a permanent outdoor exhibit that resurrects the heyday of the dinosaur-dominated Jurassic and Cretaceous Periods. Shaded within a city-block-sized canopy of old trees, velociraptor spreads its turkey-sized wings in search of carrion, the giraffe-like brachiosaurus explores the ground looking for its daily requirement of 800 pounds of vegetation, and the predator *Tenontosaurus* is captured in

a "winner take all" struggle with the clawed and terrible carnivore deinonychus. In all, sixteen different species make up the population along the Dinosaur Discovery Trail.

Fossil footprints at the museum are proof that dinosaurs walked, fought, and died in the muddy landscapes of Virginia's former coastal areas. A four-imprint trackway, part of a trail composed of 2,000 footprints made nearly 200 million years ago across an extensive swampy plain near present-day Culpeper, was created by the largest meat-eating dinosaur found in the Commonwealth to date. Named *Kayentapus*, this apex predator of the Jurassic world measured some 30 feet in length—longer than a London bus—stalked its prey on two legs while maintaining a pace length greater than 4 feet, and left in its wake three-toed footprints nearly 2 feet long. Because dinosaurs initially appeared on Earth around 230 million years ago, the size of these imprints are evidence that this class of terrible lizard grew very big very quickly. The size and shape of these and other dino tracks, along with bones found elsewhere in the United States, helped paleontologists sculpt the realistic replicas that appear around every bend of the trail.

Populated by the lifelike tyrannosaurus, the massive sail-like-spined *Spinosaurus*, and the African elephant–sized and easily recognizable triceratops, the Dinosaur Discovery Trail is the go-to place whenever an impulse arises to return to that time when ferocity was the order of the day and prey smaller than a donkey had a very uncertain future.

In replicating the inhabitants of the Dinosaur Discovery Trail, scientists estimated the texture and color of skin and other body features. –Courtesy of Virginia Living Museum

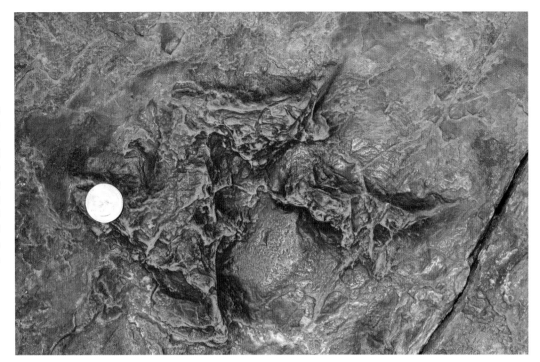

Dinosaur bones have yet to be found in the State of Virginia, but this real fossil footprint, on display in the visitor center, is proof that dinosaurs once roamed the woods and shoreline of the Commonwealth. Quarter for scale.

Similar in size to a contemporary goose egg, this replica is representative of the oldest dino eggs found to date. Estimated to be 190 million years old, placing them in the Early Jurassic Period, these eggs were discovered in China and South Africa. –Courtesy of Virginia Living Museum

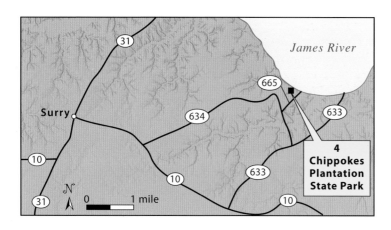

 # CHIPPOKES PLANTATION STATE PARK
Home of Virginia's State Fossil
37° 08' 45" North, 76° 44' 21" West

From 10 to 4 million years ago, during the late Neogene Period, one particular variety of scallop made its presence known above and beyond the other forms of life that populated the Atlantic coastal plain of North America: it was nearly symmetrical in construction, larger than the average saltwater shellfish—so large that during colonial times it was often used as a drinking water ladle—and found in uncommon abundance along the shoreline of Chesapeake Bay, the largest estuary in the United States.

English naturalist Martin Lister immortalized the Chesapeake Bay scallop in 1687 when he included an image of it in *Historiae Conchyliorum*, liber III, his classic study of fossils. It was the first New World fossil ever illustrated in a scientific publication. In 1824 the English geologist John Finch assembled a collection of specimens from the vicinity of Yorktown, Virginia, and sent them to scientists at the Academy of Natural Sciences of Philadelphia. There, Thomas Say, an American naturalist, formally described and named the creature *Pecten jeffersonius*, a binomial designation in honor of Thomas Jefferson, the third president of the United States. Jefferson was a naturalist of such acclaim, with a particular interest in

fossils of the New World, that he is often called the father of North American paleontology. A century and a half later, *Pecten* was assigned to the new genus *Chesapecten*, and in 1993 *Chesapecten jeffersonius* was designated the official fossil of the Commonwealth.

Specimens of *Chesapecten jeffersonius* can be more than 5 inches in length and width, making them quite large for scallops. Living in the shallow waters of the continental shelf, this scallop was quite capable of sudden movement by flapping its valves together, creating jet propulsion that safely distanced it from predators. Neogene life was good for the scallop, but then a cooler climate invaded the Commonwealth as Pleistocene-age ice sheets formed in Canada. By the time these glaciers had melted to the north, *Chesapecten jefffersonius* had been extinct for at least 3 million years.

Specimens of *Chesapecten jeffersonius* are readily found along the James River shoreline of Chippokes Plantation State Park, open dawn to dusk in Surry County. Fossilized barnacles, shark teeth, and oysters, among others, round out the list of beach fossils that one can observe along the Fossil Walk. Collecting a representative set of fossils is permitted.

The river shoreline at Chippokes Plantation State Park is littered with a mosaic of shells, evidence of the extensive range of life that inhabits—and has inhabited—this transitional freshwater-to-marine environment. Pen for scale.

Among the more unusual fossils seen at the park are barnacles, shallow-water marine animals that can be traced back to Cambrian-age ancestors. Considered "fouling" organisms today, they often attach themselves to synthetic structures, such as boat bottoms. Nickel for scale.

Front and back shell of Chesapecten jeffersonius. The nine to twelve prominent radiating ribs readily differentiate this extinct Virginia state fossil from other species of Chesapecten, which have many more. Pen for scale.

5 YORK RIVER STATE PARK
Low-Tide Collecting at Fossil Beach
37° 24' 38" North, 76° 42' 19" West

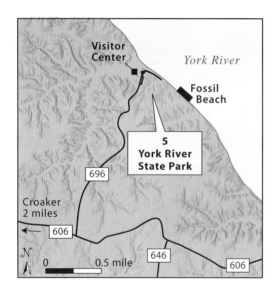

When English naturalist and physician Martin Lister included a drawing of the scallop *Chesapecten* in a study of mollusks published in 1687 (see site 4), he introduced Old World paleontologists to the Coastal Plain of Virginia, a New World locale that has been a preeminent fossil-collecting site for 330 years.

Underlain by a wedge of sedimentary rock that increases from a feather-edge thickness along the Fall Line to more than 10,000 feet at the outer edge of the continental shelf, the Coastal Plain is capped by formations deposited in warm, shallow seas during the Neogene Period. One of these units, the Eastover Formation, a 15-to-80-foot-thick sequence of tan-to-pale-yellow silty sand and gray clay, extends south from Maryland to North Carolina and as far inland as the capital city of Richmond. At York River State Park, about 45 miles east of Richmond, the sandy cliffs along Fossil Beach are rife with late Miocene–age Eastover Formation fossils.

Chesapecten jeffersonius, the state fossil of Virginia, is of course present, along with its cousin *Chesapecten middlesexensis* and other representatives of marine life that flourished along the Atlantic coastline long before the Ice Age cast a chilling pall across North America. Park visitors can find five different clams—*Dalacra*, *Mercenaria*, *Lirophora*, *Panopea*, and *Isognomon*—but the discovery of the extinct snail *Ecphora* and the "turret snail" (meaning long-spired) *Turritella* can turn a casual visit into a eureka moment of adventure. *Ecphora*, prized by both amateur and professional fossil collectors for its most unusual form and beautiful earth-toned shell, looks like it fell into a high-speed blender while in the process of forming its exoskeleton. These predator snails bored holes into the shells of other mollusks, and often even their own brethren, to feed on the soft inside tissue of their victims. The convex whorls of *Turritella*'s shell cause it to resemble a corkscrew. Fossilized barnacles, corals, oysters, and uncommon, indescribable whale bone and porpoise fragments can also be found.

Fossil-collecting permits and guide sheets are available at the visitor center. Low tide is the ideal time to visit Fossil Beach, especially after a storm has scoured fresh Miocene-age fossils from the riverside cliffs.

Forming a layer 3 feet thick at the base of a 20-foot-tall riverside cliff, this cornucopia of spiraled, 7-million-year-old Turritella shells is the signature attraction of Fossil Beach. Quarter for scale.

Mercenaria (large clam shells), the extinct predator snail Ecphora (top center), and the "screwed-up" snail Turritella (bottom row) are the "big three" Fossil Beach treasures at York River State Park. Quarter for scale.

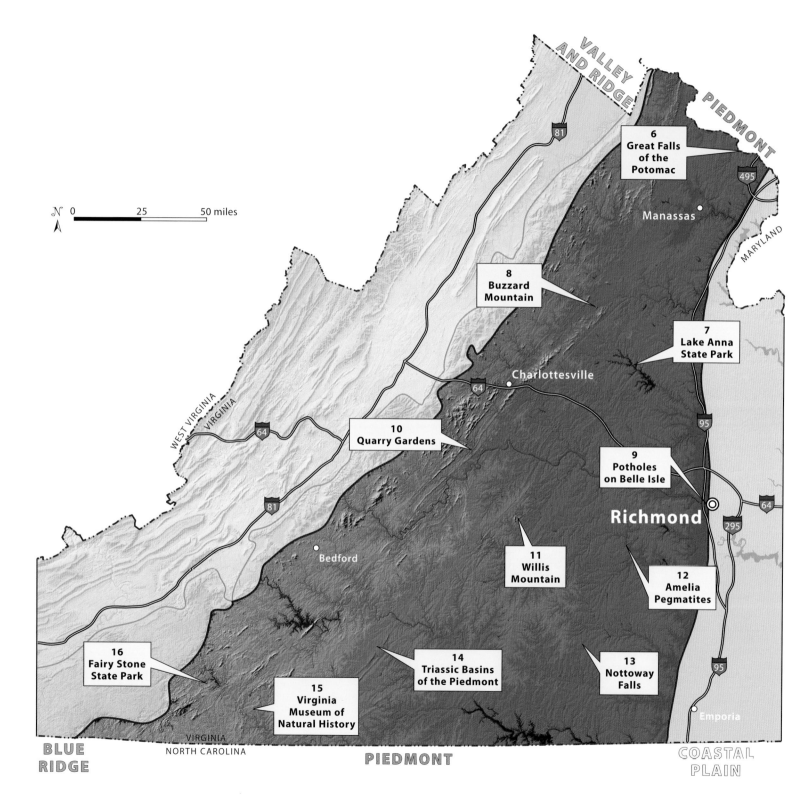

VALLEY AND RIDGE

PIEDMONT

81

6 Great Falls of the Potomac

495

Manassas

MARYLAND

8 Buzzard Mountain

7 Lake Anna State Park

Charlottesville

64

95

10 Quarry Gardens

9 Potholes on Belle Isle

WEST VIRGINIA
VIRGINIA

64

Richmond

81

295

64

Bedford

11 Willis Mountain

12 Amelia Pegmatites

16 Fairy Stone State Park

14 Triassic Basins of the Piedmont

13 Nottoway Falls

295

95

15 Virginia Museum of Natural History

VIRGINIA
NORTH CAROLINA

Emporia

BLUE RIDGE

PIEDMONT

COASTAL PLAIN

N

0   25   50 miles

PIEDMONT

The Piedmont is the largest of Virginia's five physiographic provinces, comprising nearly thirty-two counties. It is bounded to the northwest by the foothills of the Blue Ridge Mountains, and to the southeast by the Fall Line, the series of East Coast waterfalls that marks the upstream limit to ship navigation.

Geologically the province is composed of granite, gneiss, and schist terranes that, over the time span of at least 1 billion years, coalesced with ancestral Laurentia, each impact adding to the landmass of the North American continent. Elongated half grabens, notched into the crystalline Piedmont basement rocks and filled with rust-toned sedimentary rock, lie scattered across this Proterozoic, Paleozoic, and Mesozoic-age basement. They formed some 200 million years ago, when the supercontinent Pangaea was being torn asunder and the Atlantic Ocean was in a juvenile stage of development. Dinosaur and insect fossils attest to the terrestrial environment of these basins. A diverse geography composed of rolling hills, nearly flat plains, and isolated elevations called monadnocks characterize the surface of the Piedmont.

The mineral resources of the Piedmont include high-quality slate, aluminum-rich ore mined in the world's largest kyanite mine, and a controversial and thus yet-to-be-developed world-class uranium deposit.

6 GREAT FALLS OF THE POTOMAC
Retreating Rapids along the Fall Line
38° 59' 45" North, 77° 15' 12" West

Many an early seafaring captain, sailing from the Old World to the New World, hoped to gain historical immortality by discovering the Northwest Passage, the long-sought-after waterway through North America that would connect Europe and Asia. Explorers investigated every river entering the Atlantic Ocean, but on each they found a waterfall marking the upstream limit to navigation—and failure.

Colonists built villages by these cascades and turned obstruction to advantage, using the white water as a source of energy to move waterwheels and power mills. In time the settlements developed into metropolitan areas that today share a common geologic heritage—they are Fall Line cities. Geologically the Fall Line is the east-facing escarpment marking the contact between the upland landscape of the Piedmont Province and the lowland region of the Atlantic Coastal Plain. It can easily be traced—on maps and on the ground—from Tuscaloosa, Alabama, to north of Paterson, New Jersey.

The Fall Line is actually a zone rather than a single, narrow line, and the rapids and waterfalls that characterize it at any given locale may extend for miles. On the Potomac River, the zone of the Fall Line extends from Great Falls Park downstream 15 miles to the geologic contact between Coastal Plain sediments and

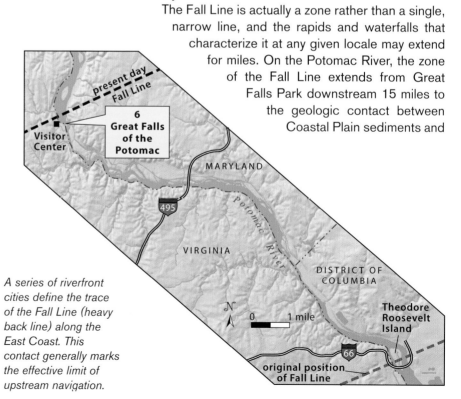

A series of riverfront cities define the trace of the Fall Line (heavy back line) along the East Coast. This contact generally marks the effective limit of upstream navigation.

The foaming and sensational rapids of the Potomac River at Great Falls Park.

Piedmont crystalline rock, exposed beneath the I-66 bridge crossing Theodore Roosevelt Island, immediately west of the Watergate Complex in Washington, DC.

Over the past 2 million years the Potomac River has eroded its channel upstream from Theodore Roosevelt Island at a recession rate—estimated by the US Geological Survey—of 1 mile every 150,000 years. The Great Falls, considered the steepest and most spectacular Fall Line rapids found on any river in the eastern United States, will continue to migrate upstream at this approximate rate. With the passage of centuries of geologic time, the turbulent, agitated waters of the Potomac at Great Falls will have evolved into a series of gentle rapids. For now, though, they are in full raging glory, as seen from the visitor center overlook at Great Falls Park.

LAKE ANNA STATE PARK
Historic Goodwin Gold Mine
38° 07' 11" North, 77° 49' 21" West

7

Virginia became a gold-mining state long before the California gold rush, when gold was discovered in Spotsylvania County in 1806. During the several decades that followed more than 290 prospects and mines became wannabe bonanza legends in the minds of men seeking fortune and fame. State production peaked in 1849 with the extraction of 6,259 ounces of gold, but intermittent activity continued until the last operation closed in 1947.

The majority of these long-abandoned sites are confined to a belt of gold-and-pyrite-bearing rock that parallels the southeastern front of the Blue Ridge Mountains, from Fairfax County to Rockingham County. Generally, the gold occurs in sulfide-rich veins and mineralized zones in deformed and metamorphosed igneous rocks—chiefly volcanic ash and lava flows—and schist, slate, and gneiss, metamorphosed sedimentary rock. The pyrite (also known as fool's gold because of its metallic, gold-like appearance) and gold are the product of contact metamorphism, chemical and mineral alteration that takes place when magma charged with volatile gas and high-temperature liquids is injected into solid rock.

Gold in the Commonwealth was initially mined from placers, river deposits in which the weathering products of gold-bearing rock have been concentrated. The process was labor intensive and relatively inexpensive: ore-bearing sand and gravel was shoveled into a trough and flushed with water that washed away the light sediment, leaving behind a concentration of dense, malleable gold in the form of flakes, grains, and even nuggets. In the 1830s a placer deposit that contained a dollar's worth of gold in a bushel of gravel was considered a bonanza mine. When placer deposits could no longer be found, miners dug pits and underground passageways, anticipating they'd discover lodes or veins—concentrations of gold in bedrock.

Little historic evidence of this gold-mining activity remains in Virginia. An exception, however, is found at Lake Anna State

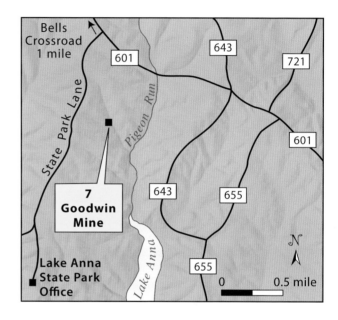

Park, in the heart of the state's historic gold country. Gold was discovered here in 1829 in the 6,000-to-10,000-foot-thick, 530-million-year-old Chopawamsic Formation, which formed during the early stages of the Taconic Orogeny, the first of the three Paleozoic-age phases of mountain building that resulted in the Appalachian Mountains.

For nearly six decades gold was produced at Lake Anna from the Goodwin Mine, using both placer and underground hard-rock mining technology. The park offers tours to the remains of a 95-foot-tall vertical shaft, stone foundations, and mounds of washed debris. The highlight of the tour, however, is the opportunity to prospect for gold using the time-tested method of washing possible gold-bearing gravel in a hand-held pan.

Managed as a surface deposit throughout most of the nineteenth century, the Goodwin Mine became an underground hard-rock operation in 1881, as evidenced by this collapsed mine shaft.

No records detail the specifics of the Goodwin operation, but ruins of stone foundations indicate where principal structures were located.

29

BUZZARD MOUNTAIN
Diabase Intrusion Sold as Black Granite
38° 19′ 39″ North, 78° 02′ 34″ West

Reminiscent of a two-humped Bactrian camel slowly disappearing beyond the horizon of its Central Asian homeland, the 150-to-200-foot-high twin peaks of Buzzard Mountain lend topographic character to the nearly flat region south of the bucolic community of Mitchells, in Culpeper County. Also known as Twin Mountain, this exposure of fine-grained igneous rock offers evidence of a marquee event of the Triassic Period: the breakup of the supercontinent Pangaea.

As Pangaea was undermined by stretch-and-pull forces similar to those crafting the present-day rift valley system of East Africa, many fault-bounded troughs were created, including the Culpeper Basin of northern Virginia. This 100-mile-long-by-10-mile-wide basin, extending from Loudoun County south to Madison County, is oriented in a northeasterly trend, parallel to the Appalachian Mountains. Magma was squeezed upward through fractures in the basin's rock and cooled and crystallized as dikes before reaching the surface. Over time erosion exposed some of these dikes, including Buzzard Mountain.

Buzzard Mountain's dual towers are more resistant to erosion than the red-toned, Triassic-age sedimentary rock in which their lower portions remain entombed. Covered with a mature growth of trees, the mountain offers excellent examples of the influence of organisms on weathering. The mountain's rock contains numerous joints filled with systems of tree roots that, through their growth, continue to increase the width of the joints. In addition, the rock surface is covered with lichens and liverworts that further enhance the rock's weathering.

Buzzard Mountain has been quarried for more than a century. Originally the rock was used as railroad ballast and for bridge abutments; more recently it has found wide application as dimension stone, such as for countertops, fountains, monuments, and tombstones. Marketed as "black granite," the rock is technically diabase, a fine-grained, light-gray intrusive rock rich in labradorite, a mineral valued for its iridescent display of color and therefore much used for ornamental purposes. Flurries of quartz veins accentuate this diabase.

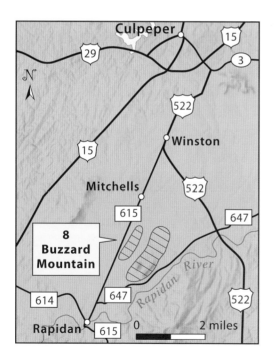

Newly quarried Buzzard Mountain diabase (jagged specimen) is light gray in color but becomes darker when polished (background example), a characteristic that gives authority to its commercial name "black granite." Quarter for scale.

Buzzard Mountain, as seen along VA 647 (Twin Mountain Road), 1 mile east of the intersection with VA 615. –Courtesy of Rachael Garrity

POTHOLES ON BELLE ISLE
Petersburg Granite Eroded by the James River

37° 31′ 26″ North, 77° 27′ 26″ West

Throughout the northern tier of America the first surefire signs of spring include crocus and daffodil blooms and . . . potholes. Seemingly appearing overnight in the form of bone-jarring pits gouged into asphalt and concrete, many believe that potholes have only existed since humans invented all-weather roads. Not true. Potholes have existed for billions of years, but prior to the automobile they formed in waterways, not roadways.

About 330 million years ago a gargantuan volume of acidic magma invaded eastern Virginia, triggered by the collision of ancestral North America and ancestral Africa, an event that heralded the onset of the Alleghanian Orogeny, the third of the three Paleozoic-age phases of mountain building that were instrumental in the development of the Appalachian Mountains. After crystallizing, this 540-square-mile pluton of Petersburg Granite remained covered by younger rock for millions of years, but erosion eventually exposed a dozen or more north-south-oriented outcrops. One exposure forms the pothole-pitted bedrock floor of the Belle Isle portion of James River Park, in the capital city of Richmond. It is 60 miles long and 5 miles wide.

Riverbed potholes typically are circular or elongate holes sculpted by well-rounded sand, pebbles, and cobbles caught up in a vortex of flowing water. They can form in any type of rock—sedimentary, igneous, or metamorphic—as long as there is a large volume of turbulent water. The Belle Isle potholes vary in diameter, from inches to over 5 feet, and harbor the gravels that helped abrade them. Some of these gravels

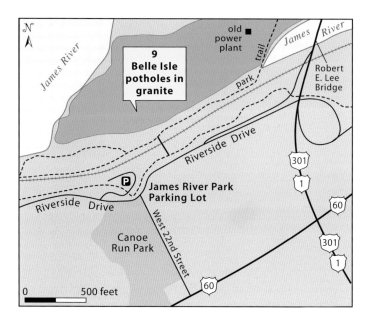

have been sourced from as far away as the Blue Ridge Mountains and the Valley and Ridge Province.

A self-guided, 1.5-mile-long tour of Belle Isle, starting at the James River Park parking lot, winds through an amazing collection of these geologic artifacts. They serve as evidence that as long as seasons change, snow melts, and water flows, there will be potholes crafted by swirling fragments of eroded rock.

The rounded granite bedrock at Belle Isle is evidence of the erosive power of sediment carried in turbulent water. Note the potholes in the foreground.

Roughly 2 feet in diameter and 5 feet deep, this Belle Isle pothole is typical of the many that have been gouged into the Petersburg Granite.

An elongate pothole that formed when two cylindrical potholes coalesced.

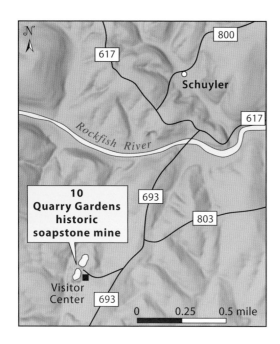

0   0.25   0.5 mile

QUARRY GARDENS
Historic Soapstone Mines
37° 46' 44" North, 78° 42' 15" West

Used for tabletops, architectural embellishments, and hearthstones, among other things, soapstone was the Vikings' rock of choice for cooking pots and is today the material Inuit natives seek out to create tribal carvings. Cocktail aficionados use "whiskey stones," cubes of soapstone cooled in the freezer, to keep their drinks chilled and undiluted by melting ice. Chemists define the pure form of soapstone as 63 percent silica, 32 percent magnesium, and 5 percent water, whereas geologists recognize it as metamorphic rock composed of excessive amounts of talc, a light-green-to-gray greasy-feeling mineral that can be easily scratched by a fingernail. Talc, the stuff of baby powder, makes easily sculpted soapstone slippery and slick. Is soapstone versatile? Very much so. Common? Not really.

Since the 1890s, the community of Schuyler, in Nelson County, has laid claim to being the soapstone capital of the world. Throughout the early decades of the twentieth century—when upscale American homes were considered incomplete without a soapstone laundry tub—seventy-five quarries in the area employed thousands of workers to produce talc-rich steatite (aka soapstone). Today, only one or two are still in operation. Glass and plastic have largely replaced soapstone commercially. A professionally designed reminder of this once viable cut-shape-and-polish industry has been resurrected in the form of Quarry Gardens. This 40-acre venue, highlighted by abandoned quarries partially filled with water, contains thirty galleries of native plants linked by 2 miles of trails that wander amongst piles of cast-aside soapstone.

Associated with 900-to-550-million-year-old metamorphic rocks of the Lynchburg Formation, Quarry Gardens soapstone was typically quarried from 100-to-200-foot-thick dikes that plunge into the subsurface at 60 degrees. Research suggests this velvety stone forms from the metamorphic alteration of various types of magnesium-rich igneous rocks, such as dunite, and by *metasomatism*. In the latter process, the dissolution and deposition of new minerals—in the space left by old minerals that have dissolved—occurs simultaneously. This process happens in magnesium-rich sedimentary rocks, such as dolomitic carbonates, and in subduction zones, where there is excessive heat and pressure and an influx of fluids. These geologic conditions are today absent in Virginia, but Quarry Gardens serves as a reminder that Nelson County was once a world-class center of a most unusual rock.

One of a pair of abandoned soapstone pits, actively mined between the 1950s and the mid-1970s, that is the central attraction at Quarry Gardens. It is estimated that some 800,000 tons of soapstone were removed from this site. Six levels of quarry-floor reduction are evident in this reflective view.

Quarried soapstone blocks, such as this 25-cubic-foot hulk, were sawed into slabs that were further finished into various shapes.

Formerly manufactured into stair treads, foot warmers, laboratory countertops, and ornamental objects, soapstone has largely been replaced by human-made materials. Its resistance to heat and acids, low electrical conductivity, and softness (note the X carved by a thumbnail), however, give it continued value as a commercial product. Quarter for scale.

35

WILLIS MOUNTAIN
11
Resistant Piedmont Monadnock Mined for Kyanite
37° 28′ 49″ North, 78° 28′ 22″ West

The Piedmont, the largest physiographic province in the state, is an amalgamation of terranes, packages of rock with distinctive geologic histories that are separated from one another by fault zones. The Piedmont is characterized by a low, nearly featureless land surface interrupted by a baker's dozen of isolated mountains, or monadnocks. One of these conspicuous monadnocks is Willis Mountain, in Buckingham County. This massif, 2 miles long, ⅓ mile wide, and 450 feet high, hosts one of the largest kyanite mines in the world.

Composed of kyanite-bearing rock of the Arvonia Formation, Willis Mountain lies in the southern sector of the Chopawamsic terrane. This minicontinent was created during the Ordovician Period, when the Taconic Orogeny, the episode of mountain building instrumental in the early development of the Appalachian Mountains, was affecting the east coast of Laurentia.

Willis Mountain's mineral recipe includes 20 to 40 percent kyanite, up to 5 percent pyrite, 0.5 to 1.5 percent rutile, and a pinch of mica and clay, with the balance being quartz. The most economically important of these minerals is kyanite, a mixture of aluminum, silica, and oxygen. It is the raw product used to manufacture refractories, heat-resistant ceramics used to line the interior of furnaces that turn iron into steel and sand into glass.

Kyanite forms in metamorphic environments, where quartz gravel, coarse sand, and silt and clay deposits are subjected to high pressures and high temperatures associated with hydrothermal fluids, heat-driven subterranean solutions. It has two different degrees of hardness: 4.5 to 5 parallel to the long axis of a crystal, and 6 to 7 across the short axis. This characteristic is unusual, as minerals normally have but one degree of hardness, defined as resistance to scratching and abrasion. On the Mohs Hardness Scale, the standard of ten minerals by which hardness is rated, talc is rated as 1, calcite 3, quartz 7, and diamond 10. In comparison, the human fingernail has a hardness of 2.5, a copper penny 3.5, and glass 5 to 6. Kyanite often develops as long bladelike crystals in radiating masses. Vitreous, pearl blue in color, and resistant to erosion, it is the very stuff that makes Willis Mountain a monadnock of industrial value.

11 Willis Mountain kyanite mine

open pit area

Dillwyn
Sprouses Corner
Areanum

0   1 mile

Kyanite is prized as a semiprecious gemstone and is one of a handful of index minerals used to estimate the temperature, depth, and pressure at which its host rock underwent metamorphism. Quarter for scale.

Kyanite usually occurs in the form of relatively long, bladelike crystals. Quarter for scale.

The southern end of the Willis Mountain monadnock, as seen from the intersection of US 15 and VA 600.

12 AMELIA PEGMATITES
Massive Crystals from the Rutherford and Morefield Mines
37° 22′ 19″ North, 77° 57′ 53″ West

Pegmatites, coarse-grained igneous rocks with a composition similar to that of granite, are abundant within the crystalline rocks that make up the Piedmont Province of Virginia. They are commonly found as irregular dikes and veins. Pegmatites contain high concentrations of minerals generally not found in commonplace granites, such as mica, rutile, cassiterite, and, to a lesser extent, gem-quality minerals, and they represent the last portion of magma to crystallize in a magma body. This more fluid magma has a high proportion of water that allows the atoms to flow freely and concentrate as gigantic crystals.

Three historic locations of industrial and gem-grade pegmatites occur in the vicinity of Amelia Court House, in Amelia County. No longer of economic value, they still house rare and valued gem minerals, such as amazonite and varieties of garnet, principally almandite, topazolite, and spessartite. The largest specimen of spessartite ever found in the area measured 3 inches in diameter, a goose-egg-sized crystal!

As of the time of this book's publication in 2019, the collecting areas were closed, but they may reopen some day in the future.

The principal zone of historic commercial operation, clustered in a 1-mile-wide belt that is 2.5 miles long, consists of twenty-one dikes and forty abandoned mines. It crosses US 360 and VA 630, 2.5 miles northeast of Amelia Court House. Dark-amber muscovite, with crystals as large as 2 by 2 feet, was the dominant money-making mineral extracted from these mines. This common variety of mica is capable of withstanding temperatures of 1,650 degrees Fahrenheit and is used as fireproofing and insulating material and as a substitute for window glass in furnaces and stoves.

In operation for nine decades, the Rutherford Mine sector, the second of the three historic mine sites, consists of a cluster of parallel dikes that are on average 30 feet wide and traceable for nearly 0.25 mile. Muscovite was the first mineral produced from this sector's mines, located 1.5 miles north of Amelia Court House, but they became famous with the discovery of amazonite, an apple-green to blue-green variety of microcline valued as a gemstone. Between 1912 and 1932, 15 tons of gem-quality amazonite was produced here, and more than fifty other rare and exotic minerals have been found at this site.

Located some 4 miles east of Amelia Court House, the world-class Morefield Mine, the third historic site, has yielded at least seventy-five varieties of minerals, a brilliant blue-green amazonite being the crown jewel of the collection. One crystal of beryl is reported to have weighed 125 pounds—an obese representative of the unusual gems associated with the Amelia Court House pegmatites.

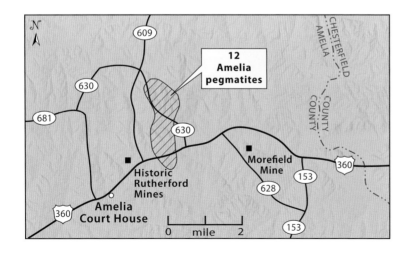

At least 200,000 pounds of potassium-rich, amber-colored muscovite were removed from the Rutherford Mine sector prior to its closing in 1959. Quarter for scale. —Courtesy of the Virginia Living Museum

This wall of blue-green amazonite, more than 5 feet in length, showcases the massive nature of the pegmatite found in the Morefield Mine. The dark-toned mineral in upper right is muscovite. —Courtesy of the Morefield Mine

39

NOTTOWAY FALLS
Waterworn Gneiss Crisscrossed with Veins and Dikes

37° 02' 47" North, 78° 08' 56" West

When mapping an area never before studied, the primary task of the field geologist is to first recognize the geological events that occurred and then place them in an orderly time sequence: which event happened first, second, and so forth. Without such organization, developing geologic history is impossible.

In 1785, while studying the igneous and metamorphic rocks that make up the Grampian Highlands of northwest Scotland, James Hutton, the Scottish geologist and naturalist widely recognized as the father of modern geology, became the first person to recognize the sequence of events that had taken place there. As a result, he is credited with formulating a basic principle useful in placing rocks and geologic events in their proper order of occurrence. The principle, called crosscutting relationships, states that any intrusive rock, such as a dike, must be younger than the rock it cuts across. This same logic can be used to develop relative ages for faults as well. For instance, a fault is younger than the rock it cuts through.

Nottoway Falls, 5 miles northeast of the community of Victoria, is a scenic and accessible area where crosscutting principles can be studied. Footpaths on the northeast side of the VA 49 bridge that crosses the Nottoway River lead to a massive outcrop of granite gneiss, a banded metamorphic rock that is the mineralogical equivalent of granite. Radiometric dating technology, which relies on the rate of decay of one radioactive element relative to another, in this case uranium to lead, indicates this water-and-sediment-polished exposure is some 295 million years old, an age affiliated with the final assembly of the supercontinent Pangaea during the Permian Period. While an absolute age has been established for this gneiss, the absolute age of the plethora of pegmatite dikes, quartz veins, and fractures that cross it has not been determined. Applying the principle of crosscutting relationships, however, is useful for determining relative ages.

The gray-toned granite gneiss was first intruded by thin dikes, followed by the intrusion of pink, coarse-grained pegmatite dikes, and then by the intrusion of blue-gray quartz veins, which were facilitated by faulting that had offset the trace of the pegmatite dikes. Smooth and shiny, the rounded profile of Nottoway Falls is a bellwether locale where the relative age relationships of features often found in intrusive rocks can be studied in detail.

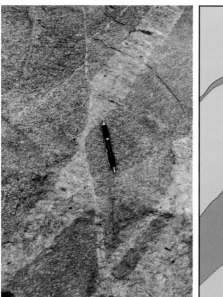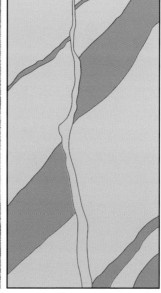

Photograph (left) and interpretation (right) of the rock at Nottoway Falls. From oldest to youngest, the granite gneiss (blue) was intruded by coarse-grained pegmatite dikes (pink) that were then laterally offset by faulting, followed by the emplacement of veins of quartz-rich rock (green). Pen for scale.

Thin, light-colored dikes (represented by the three above the pen) intruded the granite gneiss first. The black holes were drilled to hold sticks of dynamite in anticipation of quarrying that never took place. Pen for scale.

Numerous examples of crosscutting relationships, such as the quartz veins cutting across the granite gneiss in the foreground, are present in the rock exposure at Nottoway Falls.

TRIASSIC BASINS OF THE PIEDMONT
Danville Red Beds
36° 56' 46" North, 79° 09' 45" West

From a geological perspective, the drive along US 29 between Danville and Arlington is an ideal opportunity to take in the rocks composing the Piedmont Province of Virginia. Multiple outcrops of gray schist and gneiss are to be expected, but the exposures of brick-red sedimentary strata may surprise some travelers. They are known as Triassic-age red beds.

Confined to a series of linear, southwest-northeast-oriented basins, red-bed exposures indent the eastern seaboard, from Nova Scotia to South Carolina. The history of one of these structural depressions, the Danville Basin in southern Virginia, is the same as that of all the others: it involves crustal fracturing and stretching, a narrative that is the exact opposite of the gneisses of the Appalachian Mountains, which were forced upward by compressional forces wrought by continental collision.

Not long after the supercontinent Pangaea had formed, during the final epochs of the Paleozoic Era, the stage was set for its destruction. Vast chambers of liquid rock rising from the mantle first domed, then stretched, and finally fractured the overlying crust. Gradually the fractures widened into fault-edged basins that slowly filled with layers of sedimentary rock known as red beds. The sandstone, siltstone, and clay of these beds are embellished with rust-toned colors due to the ferric iron—generally less than 5 percent by rock volume—that coats individual grains. Danville Basin red beds, like those in all the Triassic-age basins along the east coast of North America, were deposited in a terrestrial environment, when Earth was enveloped in a warm, moist climate and landscaped with luxuriant vegetation.

Red-bed basins are like the geologic "stretch marks" of Pangaea's disintegration, evidence of the power of the deep-seated pull-apart forces of extension responsible for the destruction of supercontinents. They also serve as evidence that the Atlantic Ocean began to open some 235 million years ago, a process that continues even today as North America and Europe are distanced from each other at a rate similar to the growth of the human fingernail. In short, wherever blushing red rock is encountered in the eastern half of the Old Dominion, it serves as a reminder that the tectonic plates defining the surface of Earth are constantly in motion, rearranging oceans and continents into new configurations.

Red sandstone from the Culpeper Basin was quarried along the Potomac River and used as a building stone. View is 6 inches across. –Courtesy of Laura Corey, US Geological Survey

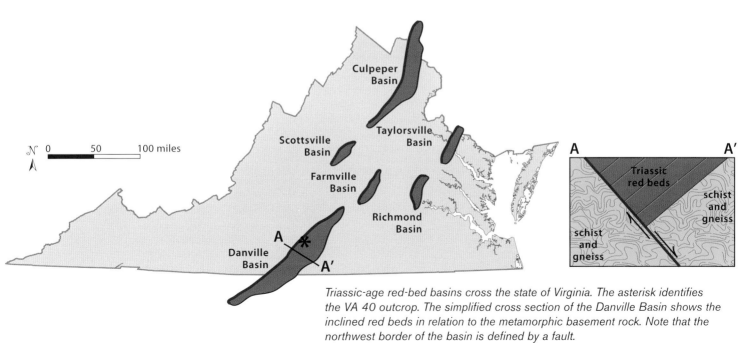

This road cut of Danville Basin strata along VA 40, 1.75 miles east of Mt. Airy in Pittsylvania County, is typical of the poorly exposed red beds of Virginia's Triassic-age basins.

Culpeper Basin

Taylorsville Basin

Scottsville Basin

Farmville Basin

Richmond Basin

Danville Basin

A
*
A′

𝒩
0   50   100 miles

A
Triassic red beds
schist and gneiss
schist and gneiss
A′

Triassic-age red-bed basins cross the state of Virginia. The asterisk identifies the VA 40 outcrop. The simplified cross section of the Danville Basin shows the inclined red beds in relation to the metamorphic basement rock. Note that the northwest border of the basin is defined by a fault.

43

VIRGINIA MUSEUM OF NATURAL HISTORY

15 Fossils from Time Immemorial

36° 41′ 12″ North, 79° 51′ 48″ West

Located in Martinsville, in the heart of the Piedmont Province, the Virginia Museum of Natural History opened its doors in 1984 as a private institution. Three years later it became an agency of the state of Virginia. Accredited by the American Alliance of Museums, a status earned by a mere 5 percent of US museums, and affiliated with the Smithsonian Institution, it holds more than ten million items in its inventory, many on permanent display in the Hall of Ancient Life, the focus of our visit.

Visitors who enter the exhibit hall with eyes focused on the fossil carcass of the 140-million-year-old allosaurus, a Cretaceous predator collected from central Wyoming, often miss the 35-foot-long *Eobalaenoptera*, an extinct species of baleen whale soaring overhead. Discovered by researchers from the Virginia Museum of Natural History, this 14-million-year-old Miocene-age skeleton of a mature adult represents a new species due to ear bone differences compared to other whale fossils of the time period. A full 50 percent of the actual skeleton has been excavated from clay and fine sand of the Calvert Formation, deposited in the Atlantic Ocean when it covered parts of Virginia and neighboring Maryland.

Nearby, novice paleontologists might mistake the 4,050-pound, 6-foot-diameter stromatolite for a flying saucer caught in a landing pattern. Estimated to be 500 million years old, the Boxley stromatolite, discovered in a Roanoke-area quarry in 2008, is representative of one of the oldest forms of colonial

Mock-up of the Miocene Epoch bone bed excavated in 1990 in Caroline County. The skull in the left foreground belongs to Eobalaenoptera, an extinct genus of whale first described by Virginia Museum of Natural History curators. —Courtesy of the Virginia Museum of Natural History

life known to exist on Earth. Specimens found in southwest Greenland date from 3.7 billion years ago, but living examples thrive in the shallow waters of Shark Bay, north of Perth, Australia. Stromatolites are layered sedimentary mounds or columns. They are the result of the growth and metabolic activity of microorganisms, principally cyanobacteria (blue-green algae), that trapped and cemented sediment in shallow water. Researchers believe the groove across the surface of the Boxley specimen may have been made by Cambrian-age herbivores, perhaps trilobites, that fed on the living cyanobacteria colony.

Not to be overlooked in the Hall of Ancient Life, the fearsome fossil skull of a tyrannosaurus is a favorite of youth and adults alike. *T. rex* is a well-known representative of the Late Cretaceous Period, weighing in at as much as 20 tons. Researchers consider its bite force—estimated to be 8,000 pounds, 40 times greater than the 200 pounds attributed to humans—the strongest of any terrestrial animal that ever existed. It was long thought that *T. rex* ruled its time as an active predator, but recent studies suggest it was instead a scavenger that fed on the flesh of dead animals and other decaying organic matter.

Additional exhibits highlight particularly fossiliferous sites in the Commonwealth. The Fossil Overlook includes exhibits of a variety of fossils, detailed models, casts, and interactive multimedia programs for visitors of all ages. Finally, the Uncovering Virginia gallery features re-creations of six research sites where Virginia Museum of Natural History scientists have worked or are presently working. Representing periods of time from 700 to 300 million years ago, video animations bring to life the animals and plants that were alive during those times.

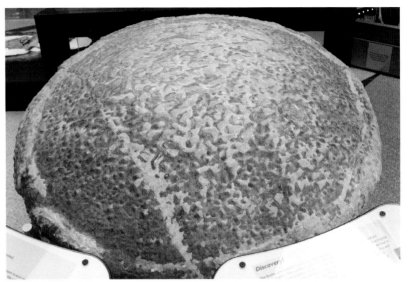

Discovered in Bedford County, this 500-million-year-old stromatolite is one of the largest intact stromatolite heads ever found.

Cast of a skull of T. rex. Pen on top of skull for scale. –Courtesy of the Virginia Museum of Natural History

FAIRY STONE STATE PARK

16

Crosses in Twinned Staurolite Crystals

36° 45′ 29″ North, 80° 05′ 28″ West

What superstition did Thomas Edison, Charles Lindbergh, Woodrow Wilson, and Theodore Roosevelt share? All four of them carried on their person one or more fairy stones, mystical keepsakes believed to bring the owner luck and protect against sickness and accidents. Spun from a legend involving frolicking fairies and an elfin messenger who arrived from a faraway city bearing the news of the crucifixion of Christ, fairy stones are said to have formed when the nymphs of the woods, saddened by the news, wept, and their tears instantly crystallized as stone crosses.

Geologically speaking, fairy stones are made of the mineral staurolite, a naturally occurring combination of silica, iron, and aluminum. Found in only a few regions in the world—and in Fairy Stone State Park, in Franklin County—people around the globe have used these brown to black minerals as good luck charms for thousands of years. They are best known for the distinctive Roman cross and Maltese cross shapes, in which rectangular crystals intersect to form perfect crosses. These are known as twinned crystals. Staurolite can also be found as single nontwinned crystals and the coveted St. Andrews cross, in which two crystals intersect to create an X.

Fairy Stone State Park specimens formed after 500-to-400-million-year-old ancestral Atlantic Ocean muds were buried to depths of 8 to 10 miles, heated to temperatures approaching 1,000 degrees Fahrenheit, and then uplifted during the Alleghanian Orogeny, one of three episodes of mountain building that formed the Appalachians. Its origins make staurolite a metamorphic *index mineral*. When geologists find it, they know that the mineral's host rock was subjected to intermediate to high-grade metamorphism, relative measures of the intensity of heat and pressure that occurred during metamorphism.

The park's official fairy stone hunt site is located 2.5 miles south of the park entrance, adjacent to VA 57. Here staurolite crystals weather out of the schist forming the northeast slope of Bull Mountain. All varieties are present, but the single version is ubiquitous and the others less common.

The display of fairy stone specimens on view at the visitor center. The two upper rows contain a mixture of Roman and Maltese crosses, the two middle rows single crystals, and the two bottom rows large and small versions of St. Andrews crosses.

Single-crystal fairy stones embedded in situ in a slab of schist. The pepper-like grains scattered across the rock surface are minute crystals of garnet. Penny for scale.

Large wooden models of the differing shapes of staurolite minerals. Left to right: Roman cross, St. Andrews cross, Maltese cross, and the single-crystal form. Penny for scale.

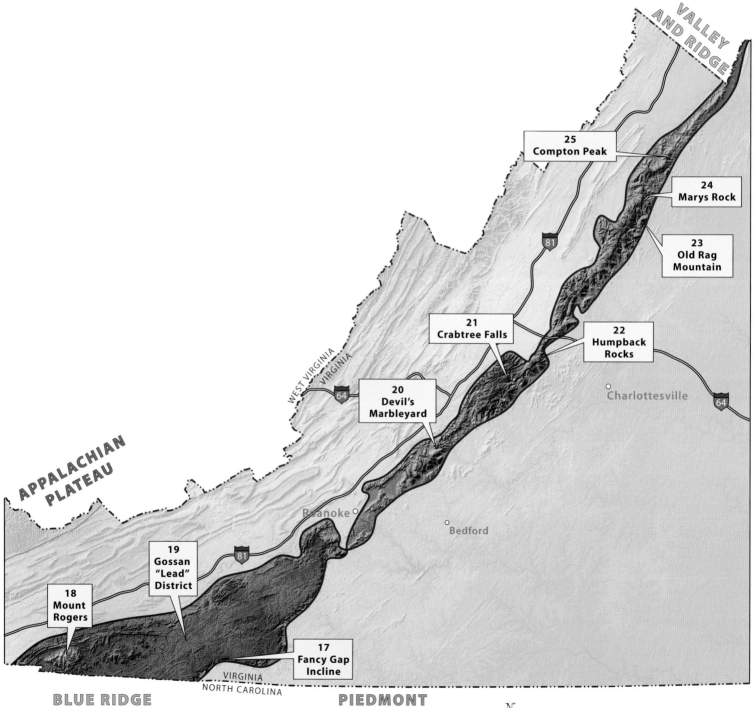

VALLEY AND RIDGE

25
Compton Peak

24
Marys Rock

23
Old Rag
Mountain

21
Crabtree Falls

22
Humpback
Rocks

20
Devil's
Marbleyard

Charlottesville

WEST VIRGINIA

VIRGINIA

81

64

Roanoke

Bedford

64

**APPALACHIAN
PLATEAU**

19
Gossan
"Lead"
District

81

18
Mount
Rogers

17
Fancy Gap
Incline

VIRGINIA
NORTH CAROLINA

BLUE RIDGE

PIEDMONT

N

0   25   50 miles

BLUE RIDGE

Viewed from afar, the Blue Ridge Province, defined topographically by the domineering Blue Ridge Mountains, is a large anticline, a convex-upward fold of rock similar to the fold that forms in a rug that has skidded across the floor. The province, and the mountain range, extending from Pennsylvania southwesterly to Georgia, borders the Piedmont Province on the southeast and the Valley and Ridge Province to the northwest. Approximately 300 million years ago this anticline-shaped landmass began to form due to compressional forces related to the collision of ancestral North America and ancestral Africa. At first it was symmetrical in outline, meaning both mountain flanks were equally inclined. Later, however, the fold became overturned—inclined so that the northwest flank became steeper than the southeast flank—due to similar forces of compression that eventually created the Appalachian Mountains and, over the course of millions of years, assembled the supercontinent Pangaea.

Formed of a now-exposed 1.1-billion-year-old core of igneous and metamorphic rock, the 4-to-25-mile-wide Blue Ridge Mountains harbor some of the greatest elevations in the Commonwealth, including the state's highest point: 5,729-foot Mount Rogers. Weekend travelers can conveniently view the geologic wonders of the Blue Ridge Province by driving the Blue Ridge Parkway, the 469-mile-long, two-lane, crest-of-the-mountain road connecting the 105-mile-long Skyline Drive, a companion roadway through Shenandoah National Park, with Great Smoky Mountains National Park to the south.

The mystique and grandeur of the Blue Ridge Mountains have long been alluded to in songs, movies, and literature. Setting romantic accolades aside, the characteristic bluish haze associated with the mountains is attributed to isoprene, a common type of organic compound produced and emitted by certain types of trees, principally oak and poplar. The mountains themselves contain a wealth of interesting minerals, rocks, and stories. For example, in 2016 nelsonite, a titanium-rich ore found in the region, was designated the official state rock.

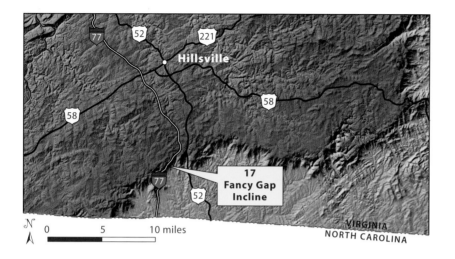

FANCY GAP INCLINE
A Descent Off the Blue Ridge
36° 37′ 22″ North, 80° 44′ 02″ West

Starting at the North Carolina–Virginia border and continuing for 6.5 miles, the Fancy Gap segment of Interstate 77 was officially dedicated in 1977. The Fancy Road, as it was dubbed in the 1850s, started as a migration route for animals that was then enhanced by Native Americans before becoming part of the interstate system. In this 1,500-foot descent travelers can see evidence of continental fragmentation and assembly, breathtaking topographic change, and drainage-basin recession.

The fragmentation of the supercontinent Rodinia at the end of Precambrian time produced two large landmasses—Laurentia (ancestral North America) and Gondwanaland. Marine sedimentary strata filling in voids separating these landmasses were ultimately subjected to several cycles of metamorphism associated with the assembly of the super-continent Pangaea during the Paleozoic Era. Alligator Back Formation, a representative of these cycles of sedimentation and compression, is the most common rock exposed along the roadside of the Fancy Gap incline. It is classified as schist—a metamorphic rock that is composed of mineral grains that have a more or less parallel arrangement and thus has a tendency to easily break into thin layers. Its distinctive sheen is formed by tiny flakes of muscovite (aka isinglass) a nonflammable, transparent mica mineral first used by the Romans to cover window openings.

On a clear day, the panoramic view from the southbound lane of Fancy Gap—considered by many one of the premier vistas of the interstate highway system—encompasses the divide between the Blue Ridge and Piedmont Provinces. Here the definition of *physiographic province*—a region with a unified geomorphic history whose relief features or landforms differ significantly from those of adjacent regions—is obvious in terms of topography more so than of geology. The relatively low relief of the Piedmont Province is a result of erosion dating back to its formation in Precambrian time, while the upland, mountainous surface of the Blue Ridge reflects a history of weathering and erosion associated with later periods of geologic time

The Fancy Gap incline is also a locale illustrative of a geomorphic process known as *recession*, the slow wasting away of an escarpment under the influence of weathering and erosion. Piedmont-based streams flowing east off the flank of the Blue Ridge Mountains have a shorter distance to travel to the Atlantic Ocean compared to Blue Ridge streams that flow north and west to the Gulf of Mexico via the New, Kanawha, Ohio, and Mississippi Rivers. The Piedmont river gradients are thus higher, and higher-gradient streams erode faster than lower-gradient streams. As a result, the hydrologic divide that passes through Fancy Gap incline is constantly shifting, or recessing, to the northwest.

Associated with fog, high-speed eighteen-wheelers, and a geologic history that dates to the earliest chapters of Earth history, the Fancy Gap incline has must-see scenery, geology, and shifting landscapes.

Muscovite is a mineral commonly found in metamorphic rocks, such as gneiss and schist. Often referenced as white mica, its minute particles lend a glossy sheen to this specimen of Alligator Back Formation. Pencil for scale.

Characterized by a highway grade approaching 5 percent, the Fancy Gap incline (note the two semis on southbound lane and one on the northbound lane) spans the contact between the Blue Ridge and Piedmont Provinces in Virginia. Roughly 18 million cubic yards of Precambrian rock had to be removed to construct the segment, making it one of the largest excavation projects in the history of the interstate system.

18 MOUNT ROGERS
Rhyolite and Rhythmite, Fire and Ice
36° 39' 36" North, 81° 32' 41" West

Mount Rogers, Virginia's highest peak at 5,729 feet, is fascinating for several reasons. When its story is discussed among professional geologists, terms such as *rhyolite*, *rhythmite*, and *dropstone* are bantered about. When the same tale is told before a lay audience, however, the terminology can be reduced to a simple phrase—"fire and ice." Mount Rogers, now home to two herds of feral mustang ponies of Spanish descent, was shaped by explosive volcanism and global glaciation, unique events in the deep-time annals of Virginia.

As deep-seated forces of extension broke apart the supercontinent Rodinia 730 million years ago, molten rock coursed upward through ever-widening fissures and erupted onto the surface. These massive flows of rhyolite, a fine-grained extrusive igneous rock characterized by 70 percent silica content, enveloped the countryside and formed the rugged topography that would become Smyth, Grayson, and Washington Counties. Mount Rogers Formation rhyolite is unusually resistant to the forces of erosion and is thus responsible for the "mountain king" status of Mount Rogers, as well as nearby Whitetop Mountain, which is nearly as tall at 5,520 feet. This explosive volcanic activity was the "fire" phase of Mount Rogers's development.

Some 650 million years ago, not long after the fire phase, at least in the geologic sense, Mount Rogers and Whitetop Mountain were glaciated—the "ice" phase. Not only did alpine glaciers sculpt the peaks, but melting icebergs, calved from the glaciers in valley-floor lakes, deposited volumes of dropstones, pea-to-tangerine-sized fragments plucked from the bedrock by the glaciers. These were dropped into what's called *rhythmite*, composed of both fine-grained sediment, deposited when the lakes were frozen, and coarser-grained sediment, deposited in open-water conditions. These layers were deposited rhythmically, perhaps on a seasonal basis. Glaciologists have cited rock packages of this type as evidence that Earth was largely covered with ice during late

Grayish 760-million-year-old Mount Rogers Formation rhyolite, which forms the bedrock throughout the Mount Rogers and Whitetop Mountain region, weathers to a mottled rust color. Quarter for scale.

Laminated rhythmite (right) and rhythmite (left) containing pea-sized dropstones (identified by scratch marks). Quarter for scale.

Precambrian time, an episode of geologic history commonly heralded as "snowball Earth."

Mount Rogers is accessible only by an arduous 9-mile round-trip hike, but ubiquitous exposures of rhyolite, along with out-of-this-world high-altitude vistas, are present at the end of 3-mile-long Forest Road 89 that winds to the top of Whitetop. In contrast, rhythmite and dropstone-bearing rhythmite are found in valley roadcuts along VA 603, east of the village of Konnarock. Fire and ice and high elevation to low elevation, the Mount Rogers region offers unique displays of Commonwealth geology.

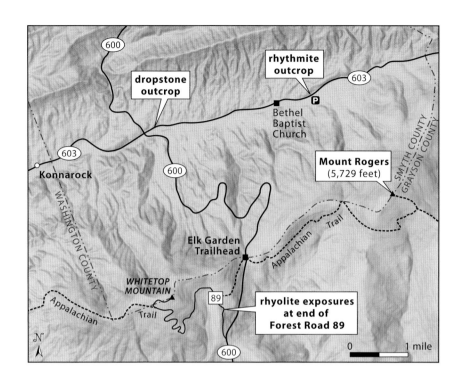

View of Mount Rogers from VA 603.

19 GOSSAN "LEAD" DISTRICT
Largest and Longest Zone of Sulfide Ore in Virginia
36° 42′ 56″ North, 80° 55′ 30″ West

After pea-sized nuggets of gold were discovered in the valley of the American River in California, more than 300,000 fortune hunters headed west and joined the gold rush of 1849. A historic event, but not unprecedented, for exactly six decades earlier a similar "rush" had taken place in Virginia. The hunters of this search weren't looking for gold but gossan, a valuable commodity that had been discovered in Carroll County.

Gossan is a rust-colored, intensely oxidized, weathered, and decomposed rock found overlying an ore zone or mineral vein. Gossan serves as evidence of an underlying metallic ore deposit, material of immense importance in the era when blacksmiths were prominent members of frontier commerce. The discovery of gossan in Carroll County led to the development of the historic Gossan Lead District, a 17-mile-long,

northwest-trending belt of discontinuous, massive zones of economic mineral deposits exposed along the northwestern flank of the Blue Ridge Mountains in southwestern Virginia. The word *lead*—a synonym of the common mining term *lode*—is pronounced "leed" and refers to a mineral deposit consisting of a zone of veins, veinlets, and disseminated veins.

In the decades prior to the Civil War, chalcopyrite (copper and iron sulfide) was the principal ore mined from the Gossan Lead District for its copper content, but after the turn of the century pyrrhotite (iron sulfide) became the mineral of choice and remained so until production ended in 1962. It was important in the production of sulfuric acid used to manufacture industrial and garden fertilizers.

Once numbering more than two dozen, Carroll County sulfide operations are now abandoned and covered in vegetation, including the massive 600-foot-long-by-300-foot-wide Bumbarger Pit. Bumbarger was a surface operation until 1925 and then an underground operation thereafter, with pyrrhotite being the principle ore. Operations at this locality began in 1789.

The remains of Bumbarger Pit are located off County Road 607, in the Iron Ridge sector of the Gossan Lead District, 4 miles north of Galax. Here, on a quiet day, with the sounds of the everyday world muted, visitors, briefly holding their breath and concentrating their thoughts, can almost hear the ghostlike clatter and clang of shovel and pickax as another boxcar load of pyrrhotite is extracted from the great Gossan Lead District.

Historic photo of entrances to the underground operations of the Bumbarger Pit in 1927. –Courtesy of the US Geological Survey, photo by Ernest Francis Burchard

Large and small blocks of pyrrhotite-rich gossan, characterized by ocherous and tawny colors and a weathered and decomposed appearance, occur along County Road 607 adjacent to the entrance to the Bumbarger Pit, which is on private property. Quarter for scale.

20 DEVIL'S MARBLEYARD
Boulder Field from Pleistocene Freeze-Thaw
37° 34' 17" North, 79° 29' 32" West

Currently the big weather story involves global warming, but not too long ago—in the geologic sense—global cooling was the ubiquitous phenomenon affecting the climate of North America. During the Pleistocene Epoch, glaciers and ice sheets greatly modified the terrain north of the Missouri and Ohio Rivers, leaving in their wake a variety of landforms. Less well known are the changes wrought in periglacial environments located just beyond the periphery of the ice masses. In these locations frost action was an important meteorological factor.

During the Ice Age a serendipitous combination of mountainous topography, fractured bedrock, and frigid weather molded high-altitude portions of Virginia into *boulder fields*, elongated accumulations of jagged, angular blocks overlying weathered bedrock of an identical composition. Several such barren vistas are known in Virginia, but Devil's Marbleyard, in

southern Rockbridge County, is exemplary in its appearance and accessibility.

How did the boulders form? The ice that invaded North America stopped short of Virginia, but harsh temperatures in front of these continental ice sheets fluctuated from above to below freezing daily. This temperature shift caused freeze-thaw weathering cycles that cracked the fissured Antietam bedrock into angular boulders.

Footstool to refrigerator in size, and countless in number, Devil's Marbleyard boulders are made of Cambrian-age Antietam Quartzite, a white, fine-grained, quartz-rich metasandstone, a sandstone that was subjected to metamorphism. Multiple examples of the trace fossil *scolithus*, straight tubelike structures dug vertically in loose sand by marine worms, tattoo the boulders. Similar fossils are found around the world in sandstones that are known to have been deposited in shallow-water environments. Some are 541 million years old. The trace fossils in the Antietam are evidence that it probably originated as beach sand in a barrier island environment akin to the modern Outer Banks of North Carolina. These worm structures are the oldest known fossils in the Commonwealth.

Boulder fields were first described in Europe, where they are termed *felsenmeer*, German for "sea of rocks." Charles Darwin famously described others in Tierra del Fuego, in South America. From beachfront property 500 million years ago to a periglacial morass of boulders today, Devil's Marbleyard exemplifies the ceaseless evolution of Earth's surface.

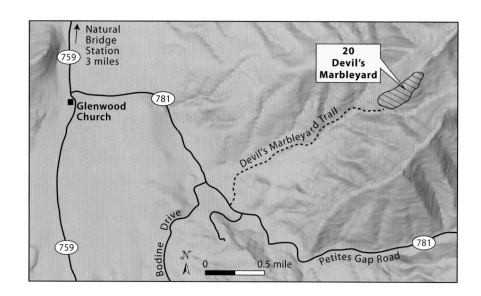

Scolithus borings were originally hollow, tubelike structures, but they filled with sand before the Antietam sediment was lithified. Typical Antietam Quartzite examples of scolithus range from slightly curved traces (left) to more distinctive straight-line traces (right, above the coin). Quarter for scale.

At first glance Devil's Marbleyard appears to be a mountain peak that was destroyed by dynamite. In reality this 8 acres of angular boulders formed through periglacial activity, specifically the long-term effects of freeze-and-thaw weathering. Hammer for scale. –Courtesy of Nathan Amick

CRABTREE FALLS
Pedlar Rock Cannot Be Taken for Granite

37° 51' 04" North, 79° 04' 47" West

Born in Crabtree Meadows, Crabtree Creek flows northward toward the Tye River, which gained notoriety when Hurricane Camille dumped 27 inches of rain across its valley in 1969 and drowned more than one hundred inhabitants. Along its course the creek forms 1,200-foot-high Crabtree Falls, in Nelson County, a series of cascades that some consider the tallest waterfalls east of the Mississippi River.

Crabtree Falls plummets over a bedrock foundation of the Pedlar Formation, composed of two types of crystalline rock, granodiorite and granite gneiss. The Pedlar defines the core

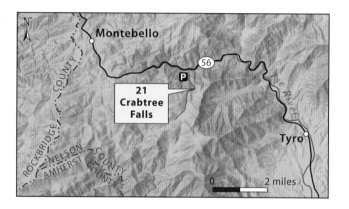

of the Blue Ridge Mountains north of the latitude of Roanoke. It formed 1.1 billion years ago, when the ancestral African and North American tectonic plates were colliding and creating the Grenville Mountains and the supercontinent Rodinia.

Viewed from askance, the Pedlar Formation has a massive, undistinguished appearance. Examined up close and personal, however, its true nature is revealed: some portions are predominantly granodiorite of an igneous origin, and others are basically granite gneiss, a type of metamorphic rock. Compared to its cousin granite, the plebeian monument and churchyard rock characterized by a "rosy-cheek" complexion brought on by potassium-rich orthoclase feldspar, granodiorite contains an abundance of calcium-and-sodium-rich plagioclase feldspar, which gives it a "pallid cheek." In fact, some 65 to 90 percent of the feldspar in granodiorite is of the plagioclase variety. The foliated nature of the granite gneiss portions of the Pedlar Formation further add to its grayish, bland appearance. *Foliation*, the planar arrangement of light and dark mineral bands, is the result of extreme temperatures and pressures that the original igneous rock was subjected to.

Crabtree Falls is composed of three distinct sections. The lowest—also the tallest at 400 feet—consists of many ledges, whereas the midpoint section plunges 80 feet through a moss-covered crevice in a single drop. At the top the upper cascade roils across a crown of weathered, dome-shaped bedrock. Rightfully heralded as an unparalleled site of spectacular geology and inspiring scenery, Crabtree Falls is one of the most-visited hiking destinations in the mountains of Virginia.

The gray complexion of the Pedlar Formation (left) is largely caused by plagioclase feldspar, whereas the rosy nature of common granite (right) is the result of orthoclase feldspar. Quarter for scale.

Crabtree Falls is actually a series of cascades ranging from vertical and free-falling water to less-steep stretches of rushing water. –Courtesy of Samuel H. Austin, Virginia Water Science Center

The lowest and tallest section of Crabtree Falls, a handicap-accessible, ten-minute walk from the parking lot, consists of multiple drops down Pedlar granodiorite, totaling 400 feet.

22 HUMPBACK ROCKS
Greenstone of the Catoctin Flood Basalts
37° 58' 06" North, 78° 53' 48" West

Geologists have separated the annals of Earth history into chapters defined by catastrophic events, such as meteor impacts, supercontinent dissection, and eruptions of *flood basalt*—outpourings of lava that bury Earth's surface on a regional scale. Well-known examples of the latter include the Deccan Flows of India, which may have caused (or helped cause) the extinction of the dinosaurs; the Siberian Traps of Russia, 960,000 cubic miles of lava that may have eliminated 96 percent of marine animals and 70 percent of land species; and, closer to home, the Columbia River Flood Basalts that cover 64,000 square miles of Washington, Oregon, and Idaho.

Though less significant to Earth's history, the Catoctin Formation is a flood basalt that helped shape the state of Virginia. Composed entirely of greenstone, basalt that has undergone metamorphism, the Catoctin Formation outcrops in belts that were initially part of a continuous layer of lava that covered more than 11,500 square miles, an area one-quarter the size of the present-day Old Dominion. Over time much of it has eroded away.

About 570 million years ago, 7,200 cubic miles of low-viscosity, iron-rich Catoctin lava flowed onto the surface of Virginia and redefined its topography. Normally an eruption like this would have been catastrophic, characterized by the wholesale death of animals and the destruction of forests, but terrestrial-based flora and fauna had not yet evolved. Nevertheless, the event is significant because the age and geographic distribution of the Catoctin Formation, extending from the presidential retreat at Camp David to Jefferson's Monticello, and from Harpers Ferry to south of Charlottesville, tell us much regarding the early geologic history of the Blue Ridge Province and the central Appalachian Mountains.

Humpback Rocks, located off milepost 5.8 of the Blue Ridge Parkway, is an exemplary exposure of Catoctin Formation greenstone. The locale is named for the "hump," created by erosion, on the western flank of Humpback Mountain.

From the summit, an exposed rock promontory at 3,080 feet that stands out from the heavily vegetated Blue Ridge Mountains that surround it, one can see from last week to well into next year. With closed eyes you can even visualize that long-ago time when 2,000-degree-Fahrenheit lava blanketed the landscape and buried hills that were more than 750 feet high.

Humpback Rocks Trail, easily the most popular hike of the northern Blue Ridge Parkway, is a light-to-moderate-difficulty, 2-mile-round-trip route with some 700 feet of elevation change. Because so many pairs of boots and shoes have traversed the summit, the rocks are not only free of the lichen that covers lower rocks, they have also been worn smooth, an unusual example of anthropologic (human-induced) erosion.

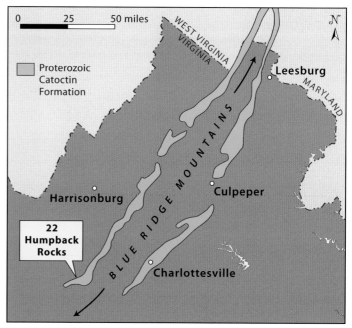

Catoctin Formation greenstone is exposed in two bands of rock that parallel the trend of the Blue Ridge Mountains, from north of Leesburg to south of Charlottesville.

Originally erupted as dark-colored lava following the breakup of Rodinia, Catoctin Formation basalt was later metamorphosed during the assembly of Pangaea. Heat and pressure formed new minerals, such as chlorite and epidote, giving the rock—now termed greenstone—a dark-green color. Quarter for scale.

Standing on the summit of Humpback Rocks on a clear day, one can see a short section of the Blue Ridge Parkway (center) and the Shenandoah Valley in the distance. –Courtesy of Nathan Amick

23 OLD RAG MOUNTAIN
Eroded Granite with Blue Quartz
38° 34' 14" North, 78° 17' 11" West

Long before the supercontinent Pangaea made an appearance, another massive landmass had achieved supercontinent status. Born some 1 billion years ago by the slow-motion amalgamation of ancestral continents, Rodinia, Russian for "homeland," remained the alpha Earth landmass for more than 400 million years.

Deep within Rodinia's bowels, pressures and temperatures created by continental collision were intense enough to transform large volumes of solid rock into a fluid mush. These bodies of magma collected in subterranean chambers, one of which was located beneath the Old Dominion. It eventually crystallized as the Old Rag Granite 1.06 billion years ago, making it one of the oldest rocks in the state. This granite is responsible for the topographic character of many of the peaks of Shenandoah National Park, the most famous being the bald-headed monadnock Old Rag Mountain.

While hiking the switchbacks up Old Rag, hikers encounter landslide debris, an 8-foot-deep crevice formed by the erosion of a dike, and a "cave" created by a massive crack in the bedrock. Hikers spunky enough to reach the 3,291-foot-high summit are rewarded with a unique rocky display of crystalline treasures and weathering features in the mountain's granite.

When deep-seated rock such as Old Rag Granite is exposed at the surface by the erosion of overlying material, it expands, due to the release of pressure, and fractures into angular blocks. Over time wind and water round the corners and edges, creating spheroidal boulders, a rock-altering process called spheroidal weathering. There are many such boulders on Old Rag.

Taking a closer look at the rock itself, one might notice that its color is not typical of other granites. Quartz, a very common mineral, is normally colorless, or smoky or rose in color, but the Old Rag Granite has a blue hue caused by the blue quartz it contains. Inclusions of rutile and ilmenite, minerals that contain titanium, are responsible for the quartz's uncommon color. An even closer examination of the rock surface reveals small reddish patches of the mineral garnet, a semi-precious gemstone that makes up some 1 percent of the rock volume. And lastly, the rock surface is pitted with shallow potholes called *opferkessel* that formed where granite has dissolved. Rainwater, augmented by organic acid from the decay of evergreen trees and lichens, formed these circular features.

An Old Rag excursion may require a vigorous hike, but the scenic vistas and geologic wonders seen along the way are well worth the effort.

This precariously balanced product of spheroidal weathering is near the summit of Old Rag Mountain. –Courtesy of Nathan Amick

When viewed at the proper angle and in the sunlight, gray quartz crystals in Old Rag Granite display shades of color that range from baby blue to light sky blue to dark grayish blue.

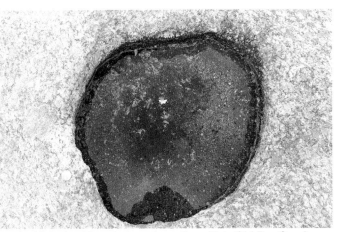

An 18-inch-wide opferkessel weathered into Old Rag Granite. Generally these pits are less than 6 inches in diameter, but some are as large as 2 to 3 feet across. –Courtesy of Nathan Amick

MARYS ROCK
Feeder Dike of the Catoctin Flood Basalt
38° 39' 06" North, 78° 18' 41" West

Marys Rock Tunnel is one of the engineering feats along Skyline Drive, the 105-mile-long byway through Shenandoah National Park. Hollowed through the crest of the Blue Ridge Mountains at mile marker 32.4 in Rappahannock County, this 610-foot-long marvel is certainly worthy of a smartphone-photo moment, but the adjacent roadside curiosity is the real attraction for visitors more attuned to tidbits of geologic history.

Pinkish, coarse-grained 1.1-billion-year-old Pedlar Formation (bottom) and fine-grained, 570-million-year-old Catoctin Formation basalt of Marys Rock dike (top). Quarter for scale.

About 600 million years ago the geographic heart of Rodinia was centered on the equator, with its coastal regions extending from 60 degrees south latitude to 35 degrees north latitude. The supercontinent was approaching old age, and tectonic forces in its underbelly were tearing it apart. During this deconstruction the deep-seated, 1.1-billion-year-old Pedlar Formation—bedrock created during the assembly of Rodinia—was fractured as two subcontinents formed. The larger of the two, Laurentia, was constructed of ancestral North America and Greenland, whereas the other, Gondwanaland, was an amalgamation of other preexisting microcontinents. In between lay the developing Iapetus Ocean, precursor to the modern-day Atlantic Ocean.

The fractures radiating through Laurentia's igneous foundation functioned as feeder conduits for the transfer of magma. Emanating from sources 50 to 70 miles deep, this magma rose and spilled onto Laurentia's surface. Within a few million years the northern regions of the Commonwealth were inundated by 7,200 cubic miles of Catoctin Formation, continental flood basalt that reinforces many of the scenic peaks in Shenandoah National Park.

One of the more impressive of these conduits intersects the north portal of Marys Rock Tunnel. Roughly 10 to 11 feet thick, this 570-million-year-old dike is easily identifiable by columnar jointing (see site 25 for more on these joints), a package of parallel, prismatic columns oriented perpendicular to the walls of the dike. The dike climbs the cliff like a ladder, with the columns, the result of contraction during cooling, acting like rungs. This dike is a textbook example of the plumbing system that birthed the Catoctin Formation, the 2,000-foot-thick cap-rock artifact of a long-ago plate-tectonic assault in northern Virginia.

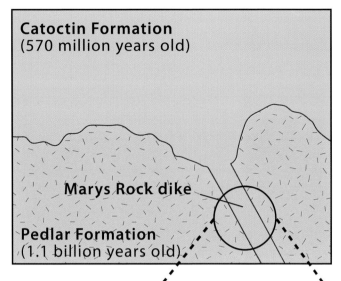

Catoctin Formation
(570 million years old)

Marys Rock dike

Pedlar Formation
(1.1 billion years old)

Cross section showing the relationship between the Catoctin Formation and the older Pedlar Formation. Marys Rock dike and columnar jointing as observed along the west side of Skyline Drive at the north portal of Marys Rock Tunnel. The field assistant is identifying the left edge of the dike. –Courtesy of Richard Wadley

25 COMPTON PEAK
Columnar Joints in Catoctin Lava
38° 49' 26" North, 78° 10' 14" West

Their presence piques the interest of both amateur scientists and seen-it-all professionals. Resembling stacked telephone poles and found on every continent, as well as in the Marte Valles region of Mars, they have been the stuff of legend from time immemorial. Nearing a count of forty thousand at Giants Causeway, in Ireland, they are whispered to be the remains of a bridge built by the giant Fionn mac Cumhaill, connecting the Emerald Isle with Scotland. Kiowa, Arapaho, and Cheyenne tribal legends explain their presence on Devils Tower, in Wyoming, as claw marks left by a giant bear chasing seven small girls who sought safety by ascending the rock mass. Variously known as prismatic structures, cooling cracks, and organ pipes, these geologic phenomena are commonly known as columnar joints.

Columnar joints are parallel, prismatic volcanic rock columns, polygonal in cross section, that generally have five or six sides but can have as few as three and as many as ten. Historically attributed to vaguely defined systems of hexagonal convection cells or isolated, ball-shaped centers of molten rock, today their origin can be compared to that of mud cracks. These many-sided, paper-thin cracks, seen in desiccated mud, are the result of shrinkage, or contraction, due to water evaporation. Similarly, tall columnar joints form as lava cools and contracts, though the volume loss isn't caused by evaporation but by the fact that cold rock takes up less room than warm rock. The change in size is greater than the strength of the rock, causing it to fracture.

An illustrative set of columnar joints is on eclectic display on the east side of Compton Peak, at the end of a moderately steep 1-mile hike from the Compton Pass parking lot, milepost 10.4 on Skyline Drive. Preserved in a 570-million-year-old lava flow, the Catoctin Formation, these columnar joints represent a chapter of destructive history, when the supercontinent Rodinia was breaking into separate landmasses. It's incredible that these volcanic structures persisted through the subsequent episodes of metamorphism associated with the building of the Appalachians and can still be viewed today, 570 million years after they formed.

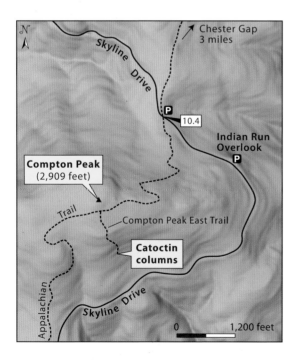

This column appears to have six sides, three of which (upper half) have been rounded by weathering. Hammer for scale. –Courtesy of Nathan Amick

As Rodinia broke apart, lava oozed to the surface, cooled, and contracted to form multisided columns composed of Catoctin Formation basalt. On Compton Peak, in Shenandoah National Park, the columns are beautifully exposed in cross section. Hammer for scale. –Courtesy of Nathan Amick

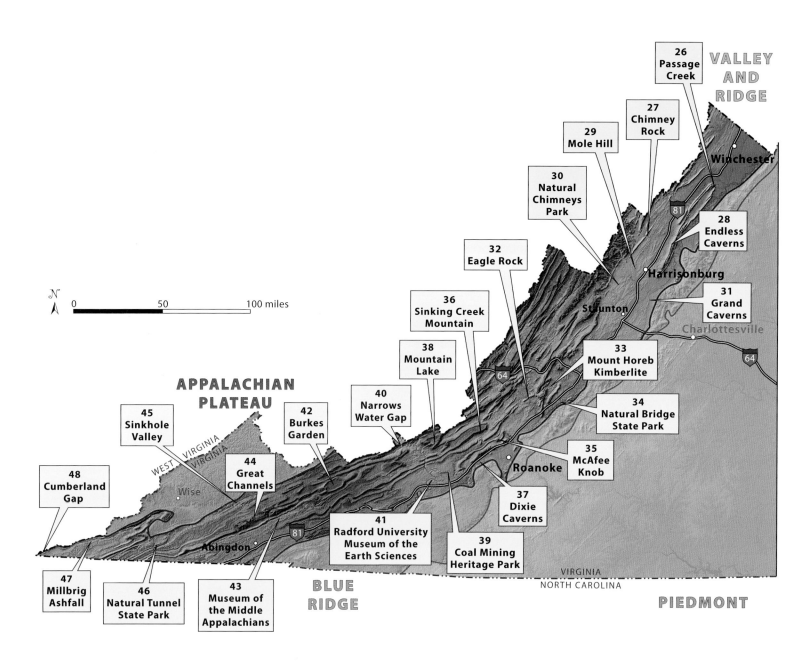

26 Passage Creek

27 Chimney Rock

29 Mole Hill

30 Natural Chimneys Park

32 Eagle Rock

36 Sinking Creek Mountain

38 Mountain Lake

40 Narrows Water Gap

42 Burkes Garden

45 Sinkhole Valley

44 Great Channels

48 Cumberland Gap

47 Millbrig Ashfall

46 Natural Tunnel State Park

43 Museum of the Middle Appalachians

41 Radford University Museum of the Earth Sciences

39 Coal Mining Heritage Park

37 Dixie Caverns

35 McAfee Knob

34 Natural Bridge State Park

33 Mount Horeb Kimberlite

31 Grand Caverns

28 Endless Caverns

VALLEY AND RIDGE

APPALACHIAN PLATEAU

BLUE RIDGE

PIEDMONT

Winchester

Harrisonburg

Staunton

Charlottesville

Roanoke

Abingdon

Wise

WEST VIRGINIA

VIRGINIA

VIRGINIA

NORTH CAROLINA

N

0   50   100 miles

81

64

64

81

VALLEY AND RIDGE

Characterized by northeast-southwest-oriented uplands separated from similarly oriented high-relief hollows, the Valley and Ridge Province is sandwiched between the Appalachian Plateau to the northwest and the Blue Ridge Province to the southeast. Composed of Paleozoic-age sedimentary rock, this physiographic system of highs and lows is the result of the differential weathering and erosion of elongated chains of strata that formed during an extensive history of folding and faulting.

Underlain by a thick sequence of carbonate rock, the Great Valley (aka the Shenandoah Valley) is characterized by well-developed karst and a system of stalactite-and-stalagmite-rich caverns that support a thriving tourist industry. In contrast, the ridges of the region are commonly capped by compacted sandstone and conglomerate that are more resistant to the forces of erosion than the softer strata of the valleys.

26 PASSAGE CREEK
Boulder Field from the Ice Age Climate
38° 56' 42" North, 78° 18' 17" West

In 1837, speaking before peers in Neuchâtel, Switzerland, Jean Louis Agassiz, renowned Swiss-born biologist, physician, and geologist, introduced a subject that quickly became controversial throughout the scientific community. He posited that Europe had once been covered with a sheet of ice extending from the North Pole to the Mediterranean Sea. Some colleagues rejected his thoughts as ill-informed. After all, his expertise was fossil fish, not ice. But others saw value in his words, especially as they related to the large boulders found high in the mountains that were composed of minerals foreign to their surroundings.

Agassiz had spent several years studying these boulders and argued they could be traced to the highlands of Scandinavia and had been transported to central Europe encased in continental-sized sheets of ice. In later years other types of evidence—such as polished bedrock and mounds of poorly sorted sediment—further supported the concept that Earth had recently, in the geologic sense of time, been subjected to a global ice age. Today, it's universally accepted that a global episode of chilled climate—the Pleistocene Epoch—occurred between 2.6 million and 10,000 years ago, leaving a landscape visually altered by the formation, movement, and recession of massive ice sheets.

Abrasion and deposition are the principal means by which continental glaciation directly impacts the landscape, the former being mechanical operations that reduce topography, and the latter those that add topography in the form of rock debris left in the wake of retreating ice. Indirect effects include isostatic uplift, the upward flexing of land after the weight of an ice sheet has been removed (that is, has melted), and global sea level rise, also caused by ice melting.

Less recognizable are periglacial effects, landscape-altering conditions created by cold temperatures near the margins of ice sheets. Accumulations of angular boulders, or boulder fields, are classic examples of landforms that developed in a periglacial climate. There are several covering the valley slopes of Passage Creek in extreme northeastern Shenandoah County.

Throughout the Ice Age, the cold winds related to the periglacial climate of Virginia swept across exposures of Silurian-age Massanutten Sandstone, the dominant rock of Massanutten Mountain. Cyclical episodes of freezing and thawing split the rock open, forming bedrock fissures that eventually eroded into a disordered accumulation of angular rock. Characterized by patches of tree-denuded slopes, the boulder fields of Passage Creek have stayed put since their formation.

Strasburg

North Fork Shenandoah River

55

Waterlick

678

55

WARREN COUNTY
SHENANDOAH COUNTY

Passage Creek

26
Passage Creek
boulder field

P

619

678

N

0   1 mile

The quartz-rich Massanutten Sandstone is technically an orthoquartzite, a clastic sedimentary rock composed almost exclusively of quartz sand. An outstanding example of a periglacial boulder field full of this sandstone can be conveniently surveyed from a small roadside parking area along VA 678, 1.9 miles south of the community of Waterlick. Quarter for scale.
—Courtesy of Rachael Garrity

Composed of refrigerator-sized blocks of Massanutten Sandstone, the boulder field at the VA 678 parking lot blankets the mountainside without appearing to have a parent source of rock material. —Courtesy of Rachael Garrity

27 CHIMNEY ROCK
Vertical Sandstone with Devonian Fossils
38° 38' 48" North, 78° 52' 05" West

One of the fundamental concepts of geology is the principle of original horizontality, which posits that rock layers found in nonhorizontal positions were, in all probability, originally deposited horizontally and later tilted. A textbook application of this rule is found 4 miles northwest of the community of Broadway, at the intersection of VA 259 and VA 612, in Rockingham County. Here the layers of Chimney Rock, composed of Ridgeley Sandstone, loom upward at a 90-degree angle to the ground one stands on to view them.

Throughout central and northeastern Virginia the Ridgeley Sandstone forms eye-grabbing landscape features. Gray in color and fossil bearing, it has been quarried to produce quartz sand for glassmaking. Geologists cannot determine its exact age because it lacks radioactive minerals, but they have determined its antiquity by methods other than radiometric analysis.

Because Chimney Rock is located in the Valley and Ridge Province of Virginia, it was elevated to its lofty position by the compressive forces of the Alleghanian Orogeny, the final tectonic episode that created the Appalachian Mountains some 300 million years ago. The precept of the principle of original horizontality tells us that the Ridgeley is therefore older than 300 million years, a limiting but not absolute date.

Fortunately Chimney Rock strata contain fossils that can further constrain the Ridgeley's age. *Platyceras* is an extinct sea snail that lived from the Ordovician through the Permian Period, and *Costispirifer* was a large brachiopod that enjoyed life *only* during Early Devonian time—approximately 400 million years ago. Eureka! The limited time span of *Costispirifer* is the defining factor for determining the relative age of the Ridgeley Sandstone. It was deposited during Early Devonian time.

Determining the age of any rock is challenging, and sometimes it's not possible, but with a little bit of information—a guiding principle and a few fossils, such as those found at this roadside site—the improbable can be made manageable.

Chimney Rock accentuates the west side of Little North Mountain and is one of many folded and tilted sedimentary rock structures that make up the Valley and Ridge Province.

Chimney Rock has a limited geologic future, as evidenced by an intersecting system of fractures that facilitate spalling, the weathering process that gradually reduces rock masses to rock fragments.

Imprints of gastropods, pelecypods, and large brachiopods are common in the blocks of Ridgeley Sandstone that surround Chimney Rock. Only peripheral remnants of a one-time complete shell (arrow) remain of this fossil brachiopod. Quarter for scale.

Water dripping from soda straws, tubular stalactites that maintain the diameter of a drop of water and resemble drinking straws. These serve as proof that cave formations are still developing at Endless Caverns.
—Courtesy of Dave from the Cave.com

ENDLESS CAVERNS
Dissolution of Ordovician Strata
38° 35' 43" North, 78° 40' 32" West

Filling the family cooking pot and empty stomachs was apparently the purpose of the autumn 1879 excursion, when two lads cornered a wily rabbit behind an outcropping of Ordovician-age limestone at the base of Massanutten Mountain, in Rockingham County, and made a discovery. The hare was quickly flushed from its intended sanctuary, but in the process the boys stumbled upon a passageway into the ground. Today it serves as the entrance to a 6-mile-long system of interconnected chambers known as Endless Caverns. Located in New Market, guided tours are offered for a nominal fee.

Thick sequences of carbonate strata that constitute the basement of the Shenandoah Valley create an ideal foundation for the development of caves. For millions of years, carbon dioxide–charged rains have fallen to Earth as dilute concentrations of carbonic acid, soaked the ground, seeped into available cracks, and slowly dissolved the limestone bedrock. Sinuous underground passageways have developed, some of great length and impressive magnitude. Numerous

expeditions have yet to find an end to the complex network of underground passageways at Endless Caverns, thus the name. On a broad scale, this dissolution results in the formation of *karst*, a distinctive topography characterized by sinkholes, underground drainage, disappearing streams, reappearing springs, and . . . caverns.

Initially swamped with water, cavern systems can become dry when either the land is elevated or the groundwater level is lowered. Once dry, a range of cavern formations, including flowstone, stalagmites, stalactites, and soda straws, begin to ornament ceilings, walls, and floors. These form as the mineral calcium carbonate precipitates from rainwater percolating into the underground voids.

Endless Caverns is a fairyland of signature limestone features: icicle-like pendants; shields, mysterious circular plates separated by thin cracks; rimstone, ruffle-like terraces that radiate across the cave floor; and semicircular grooves worn into the limestone walls, remnants of channels long ago eroded by subterranean, cavern-developing streams.

Reminiscent of the aftermath of a winter storm, the Snowdrift, the largest carbonate formation in Endless Caverns, appears as a great drapery of ceiling-to-floor flowstone that is slowly enveloping a cluster of earth-toned pillars. —Courtesy of Dave from the Cave.com

A column forms when a stalactite and stalagmite join, or when either grows all the way to the ceiling or the floor. The crack in the center of this flowstone-anchored column is attributed to earthquake vibrations. —Courtesy of Dave from the Cave.com

MOLE HILL
Remnants of a Volcano
38° 26′ 58″ North, 78° 56′ 36″ West

The cataclysmic eruption of Mount St. Helens in 1980 awakened Americans to the fact that volcanic activity was alive and well in the United States. Since then many have become even more aware of the country's relatively recent volcanic phenomena: Yellowstone National Park is home to an irascible supervolcano, Idaho's Craters of the Moon National Monument formed during eight major eruptive periods between 15,000 to 2,100 years ago, and the determination that Sunset Crater erupted circa AD 1085 has been a wake-up call to the residents of Arizona. But these events happened out West. Americans living east of the Mississippi River generally don't worry that much about volcanism. Learning about Mole Hill, however, might change their point of view.

Rising 400 feet above the bucolic landscape of Rockingham County, tree-covered Mole Hill is crowned by exposures of basalt, a dense igneous rock associated with volcanic activity. Its fine-grained texture is characterized by peppercorn-sized crystals of olivine, one of the first minerals to form when molten rock cools. For well over a century geologists assumed this rock was old. It was thought to be either 300 million years old, the product of the extensive volcanic activity associated with the building of the Appalachian Mountains, or at least 200 million years old, having formed when the supercontinent Pangaea broke up and gave birth to North America, Africa, and South America. When analyzed using modern age-dating processes, however, the basalt was found to be no older than 47 million years, a very youthful age, considering Earth is 4,600 million years old.

Mole Hill is not the only evidence of recent volcanic activity in northwest Virginia, although it's the largest. Nearby Trimble Knob, in Highland County, is composed of rock similar to that at Mole Hill, and roughly one hundred exposures of yet-to-be-analyzed rock tattoo the surrounding countryside.

The jury is still out as to how Mole Hill evolved. One theory relates it to a hot spot, a rising plume of molten mantle material that erupted as a volcano, a process similar to how Kīlauea is forming in Hawaii today. A second suggests volcanic activity associated with a little-known earthquake belt that was responsible for the 5.8-magnitude quake that rumbled through northern Virginia in 2011. There is consensus, however, that Mole Hill is the eroded and weathered remains of a plug, a vertical, pipelike body of cooled magma that represents the conduit of a former volcanic vent. Its horizon-producing presence and exceptional youthfulness—in the geologic sense—are proof that volcanism, and its devastating effects, might yet have an impact on the landscape and population of the Commonwealth.

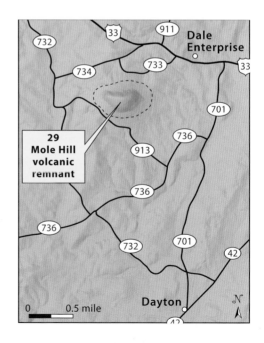

Looking northwest at the private property of Mole Hill, from Swope Road (VA 736).

Mole Hill volcanic rock is identified by peppercorn-size crystals of olivine and an occasional larger inclusion of country rock (right of the coin). The latter is a fragment of the deep-seated sedimentary rock the Mole Hill magma intruded. Penny for scale.

Light-to-medium-gray, 450-million-year-old Beekmantown Dolomite forms the sedimentary country rock the magma intruded about 47 million years ago. Penny for scale.

Natural Chimneys is thought to resemble the turrets of a foreboding medieval castle, so an annual jousting tournament–competitions between mounted modern-day knights using a variety of weapons–has been held beneath the looming towers since the 1820s.

NATURAL CHIMNEYS PARK
Limestone Turrets with Nodules and Dikes
38° 21′ 30″ North, 79° 04′ 59″ West

Limestone is an amazing rock. By volume it constitutes 10 percent of all the sedimentary strata on Earth. Durable and relatively hard, it's used as a dietary supplement for cattle and chickens, as a pigment in toothpaste, in the production of cement and lime, as gravel and riprap material in the construction industry, and as a building stone for both skyscrapers and patio floors (after having weathered to a pleasing patina). Circa 2,570 BC, Egyptians used 2.3 million blocks of it to construct the Great Pyramid of Giza.

Limestone forms principally in clear, shallow, warm marine environments from the accumulation of calcium carbonate shells and coral, as well as algae and fecal debris. It can also form by the precipitation of calcium carbonate from lake or ocean water. Found throughout the world, in the Shenandoah Valley it can be found at Natural Chimneys Park in Mt. Solon, in Augusta County.

Known also as Vulcans Forge and Cyclopean Towers, Natural Chimneys is an extraordinary collection of seven imposing rock structures whose story begins with the deposition of the Conococheague Formation some 500 million years ago, during the Cambrian Period, when the region was inundated by an inland sea. For millions of years this 2,000-foot-thick mass of calcium carbonate lay undisturbed, but then it was caught in the tectonic grip of the deep-seated forces that created the Appalachian Mountains. Rock massifs were shoved upward, folded, and physically altered to include an interconnected system of vertical cracks and fissures. Finally, stringers of magma were injected into the limestone, the result of volcanic activity occurring 10 miles to the north (see site 29). Radioactive analysis indicates the igneous rock is 49 million years old, making it approximately 450 million years younger than the limestone it intruded.

Over time, rainwater and groundwater have percolated through the cracks, dissolving and wearing away susceptible areas to the degree that only a network of tunnels and 60-to-120-foot-high towers remain. Natural Chimneys is a geologic curiosity unique in the eastern United States, and it is also an ephemeral one, as it is destined to be erased by water, the same essence of nature that created its rock foundation.

Irregularly shaped nodules of chert embedded in Conococheague limestone formed from clusters of silicon dioxide microcrystals that were compressed. Originally these microcrystals stiffened and supported the tissues of various marine invertebrates. This eye-level example is 3 inches wide.

A dark-toned, 7-to-12-inch-thick sill of 49-million-year-old volcanic rock (center) can be traced from an eruption center located 10 miles to the north.

31 GRAND CAVERNS
Solution Features in Vertical Cambrian Limestone
38° 15′ 32″ North, 78° 50′ 05″ West

Discovered in 1804 and opened to the public two years later, Grand Caverns, in Grottoes in Augusta County, is America's oldest continuously operating commercial cavern. It is one of more than four thousand cavern systems known in the Commonwealth. Grand Caverns zigzags almost 4 miles through Cambrian-age rock of the Conococheague Formation, in the Shenandoah Valley, the lowland Valley and Ridge region lying adjacent to the Blue Ridge Mountains.

Like other cavern systems in the Valley and Ridge, Grand Caverns formed as acidic groundwater and precipitation dissolved limestone. It harbors a plethora of deposits commonly found in subterranean chambers: flowstone, stalactites, stalagmites, helictites, and columns. Two particular features, however, distinguish Grand Caverns from other commercial caverns in the Shenandoah Valley: nonhorizontal structure and ubiquitous shields.

Cavern systems often develop in rock that has remained undisturbed from the horizontal orientation at which it was deposited. In contrast, Grand Caverns formed within 500-million-year-old rock that stands on end, an upright position caused by continent-crunching compressive forces associated with the birth and growth of the Appalachian Mountains.

Shields are composed of two parallel discs separated by a thin, planar space through which water circulates. Opinions differ as to how shields form, but the most accepted theory relates to the presence of fractures. Water under pressure moves through thin bedrock fractures, enters a cave passage, and deposits calcium carbonate on either side of the fractures, creating plates of calcite that grow outwardly and radially along their rims and are separated from each other by a thin water-filled space. Shields are found in at least 80 caves in the United States, but in Grand Caverns they are especially abundant: more than 250 of these giant clam-like calcite formations project from the walls, ceiling, and floor.

Grand Caverns is beautified by a range of colors. A thin coating of iron oxide adds a blushing tone to the white hue of the calcite formations. Algae growth fueled by dampness, light, and heat adds a green tint to the otherwise battleship-gray limestone.

Attributed to water flowing down an inclined cave ceiling, draperies form a sinuous trail of calcite that looks like heavy fabric arranged in loose, undulating folds. –Courtesy of Grand Caverns

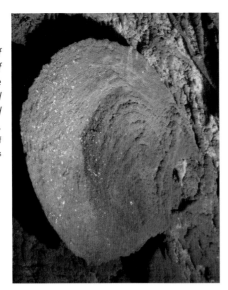

Hundreds of rare shields of varying size can be found in Grand Caverns. –Courtesy of Grand Caverns

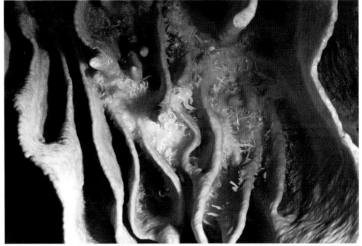

Helictites compose a diverse group of cave deposits that grow in any direction, seemingly defying gravity, and assume quirky forms, ranging from minute filaments to thick, antler-like shapes. –Courtesy of Grand Caverns

The waxy appearance of this 7.5-foot-tall stalagmite, affectionately known as the Ghost of George Washington, is associated with earlier occasions when it was ceremoniously decorated with costumes and wigs. Oils left behind by human contact have completely stopped its growth. –Courtesy of Grand Caverns

32 EAGLE ROCK
Convoluted Folds and Faults, Appalachian Style

37° 38′ 29″ North, 79° 48′ 24″ West

Like hair, mountains exist in a variety of styles. Volcanic mountains are created when magma erupts onto the surface and piles up (Mount St. Helens), whereas dome mountains form when magma pushes up from below Earth's crust (Black Hills). Fault movements triggered by tension rearrange large chunks of Earth's crust and create block mountains (Sierra Nevada), whereas plateau mountains are sculpted by water and wind eroding topographic relief into flat regions (Catskills). The most common type of mountain, however, is the fold mountain, crafted by the head-on collision of continental tectonic plates, like automobiles smashing together (Alps, Himalayas, and the Appalachians).

The Appalachian Mountains have conceivably been studied to greater extent than any other high-relief region of the world. Early on researchers erroneously thought its folded rocks resulted from the cooling of a molten Earth. The cooling resulted in contraction, and pressure created by contraction caused parts of Earth's crust to buckle upward forming mountains, an effect compared to the wrinkled skin of a drying apple. This shrinking Earth theory could not, however, explain why mountains are unevenly distributed across continents.

In 1912, Alfred Wegener—the father of the continental drift theory—proposed an alternate explanation when he introduced the idea of Pangaea, a supercontinent that broke up some 200 million years ago into landmasses that "drifted" apart. Compression associated with the leading edge of each subcontinent led to the formation of fold mountains. This explanation helped explain the coastal distribution of many mountains and their different ages but failed to identify a force powerful enough to fracture a supercontinent.

Then came plate tectonics theory. By the mid-1960s, this theory had been accepted by most members of the scientific community because it had passed a great many tests and had tremendous predictive power. One of its tenets states that fold mountains form when tectonic plates collide, creating folds in the sedimentary rocks distributed along their margins, similar to the folds you might see in a rumpled rug that has been pushed across the floor.

Plate tectonics theory adequately explains the broad-scale development

The road sign seems to say it all: DO NOT ENTER into an attempt to interpret the topsy-turvy geology of these rocks, because you'll surely arrive at a WRONG WAY answer.

SOUTHEAST

NORTHWEST

32
Eagle
Rock

220

fault

Simplified interpretation of geology as seen from the James River bridge. The white line represents a folded fault plane, with the relative movement of each fault block indicated by arrows.
–Modified from McGuire, 1970

Devonian rocks

Devonian and
Silurian rocks

Silurian rocks

View toward US 220 and the massive exposure of Eagle Rock strata, from the center of the James River bridge outside Eagle Rock.

of fold mountains, but a clearly defined explanation can be difficult to arrive at when one is confronted with a convoluted roadside exposure of rock. An excellent example of Appalachian rock sans a clear origin story outcrops along the James River outside Eagle Rock, in Botetourt County, adjacent to the junction of US 220 and VA 43.

At first glance, interpreting the geology of this electrifying wall of rock, composed mostly of sandstone with interbedded shale, limestone, and conglomerate, seems a simple exercise in analyzing rock structure. Up close and personal, however, the task becomes confusing. Does this several-blocks-long

exposure represent a pair of recumbent anticlines, convex-upward folds that were compressed to the degree they now lie on their sides, or is it a syncline, a concave-upward fold, broken by faults that stack one sequence of sedimentary rock upon another like shingles on a roof?

As always, the devil is in the details, and this outcrop seems to constitute an inexplicable and seemingly unsolvable example of inscrutable fold-mountain construction. Short on answers yet pleasing to the eye, the Eagle Rock exposure will remain, for the foreseeable future, a must-see example of a rock-bound enigma waiting for a solution.

33 MOUNT HOREB KIMBERLITE
A Possible Diamond Source

37° 42' 50" North, 79° 38' 22" West

In the 1953 film *Gentlemen Prefer Blondes*, Marilyn Monroe expresses her undiluted admiration for the hardest-known mineral when she sings "Diamonds Are a Girl's Best Friend." Jewelry aficionados also treasure this unique arrangement of carbon atoms for several reasons: its ability to disperse light of different colors, high luster, and reputation as the world's most popular gemstone.

Few diamonds are produced in the United States. There is a tourist mine operated by the State of Arkansas on a keep-what-you-find basis and a small amount was commercially produced during the 1990s in north-central Colorado. Four specimens have been found in Virginia, and a fifth—a bluish-white giant weighing 34.48 carats—was discovered along Rich Creek, in Peterstown, West Virginia, less than 1,000 feet from the Virginia state line. All were recovered from unconsolidated sediments and were probably transported some distance from their parent source. The Mount Horeb kimberlite, however, is one in situ locale that might contain diamonds—emphasis on *might*.

Kimberlite, named after the historic diamond mines near Kimberley, South Africa, is an igneous rock that sometimes contains diamonds. Created under extremely high temperatures (in excess of 1,450 degrees Fahrenheit) and pressures (greater than 1 million pounds per square inch) at depths of about 100 miles beneath the surface, in Earth's mantle, the diamonds are brought to the surface by deep-seated volcanic explosions that erupt through breccia-filled conduits, passageways filled with angular, broken rock fragments.

The Mount Horeb kimberlite consists of three separate intrusions into the Ordovician-age Beekmantown Dolomite that underlies the forested southwest flank of Mount Pisgah. Weathered exposures occur opposite the Mt. Horeb United Methodist Church on VA 807, in Rockbridge County. No diamonds are found here, but so-called indicator minerals such as garnet, diopside, and ilmenite have reportedly been found in the stream that flows through the churchyard. These minerals form with diamonds in Earth's mantle, and their presence indicates that diamonds may also be present.

The Mount Horeb kimberlite has zero commercial value, but as a "not-impossible" source of valued gemstones it remains a site of interest. It most definitely has value as an example of the mysterious mineral transformations that take place in the deep depths of Earth.

The weathered contact of the Mount Horeb kimberlite and Beekmantown Dolomite lies partially buried in the wooded hillside alongside VA 807 (upper right). Panning in the nearby churchyard drainage (bottom left) has yielded minerals suggestive of, but not proof of, the presence of diamonds.

Naturally occurring diamonds can be colorless (left, 8.21 carats) or have a range of colors, including black (center, 1.45 carats), commonly caused by inclusions of graphite, and sunshine yellow (right, 5.47 carats), attributed to the presence of nitrogen.
–Courtesy of Crater of Diamonds State Park, Arkansas

Mount Horeb kimberlite is characterized by indicator-mineral inclusions, as seen in the rock specimen on the left and the distinctive orange-weathered surface of the example to the right. Quarter for scale.

34 NATURAL BRIDGE STATE PARK
An Arch Formed by Karst Erosion
37° 37' 41" North, 79° 32' 41" West

It is estimated that karst, a type of landscape formed by the dissolution of soluble rock such as limestone, dolomite, and gypsum, affects more than 20 percent of America's land surface. It is characterized by sinkholes, springs, caves, and disappearing streams and rivers. Such well-known attractions as Carlsbad Caverns in New Mexico, Jewel Cave in South Dakota (the third-largest cavern in the world), and the roly-poly topography of the Bluegrass Region of Kentucky developed in karst. Setting aside the tourist income related to karst, on average it causes more than $300 million annually in infrastructure damage in the United States, exemplified by a 1981 Florida sinkhole that catastrophically consumed five Porsches, an Olympic-sized swimming pool, and a three-bedroom home in the course of one day.

Karst extends through portions of twenty-nine of Virginia's ninety-five counties, as evidenced by some 4,300 caves and close to 49,000 sinkholes. The best-known karst-related attraction in the Commonwealth is Natural Bridge, famously described by Thomas Jefferson, the third president of the United States, as a "convulsion of nature." However, there is general agreement these days that karst isn't fully responsible for the creation of Natural Bridge. Cedar Creek, the stream that placidly flows under the arch, played a role.

Several million years ago an elongate sinkhole developed near Cedar Creek, redirecting it. Once a tributary to Cascade Creek, Cedar Creek flowed into the sinkhole, becoming a subterranean stream. Eventually this subterranean channel extended its reach by dissolving 470-million-year-old Beekmantown Dolomite and Chepultepec Formation limestone, the final outcome being the creation of a tunnel. Most of the tunnel roof collapsed long ago, leaving Natural Bridge as the only surviving remnant and allowing Cedar Creek to once again flow at the surface and into Cascade Creek.

In the not-too-distant geologic future this remaining tunnel segment will also be reduced to rubble by erosion and weathering, the enemies of all rock. So don't wait. Head to Natural Bridge State Park, in the town of Natural Bridge, to have a look yourself.

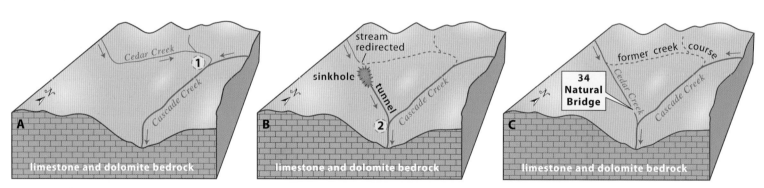

(A) Originally Cedar Creek was a tributary to Cascade Creek (1), but (B) a nearby sinkhole redirected it into a subterranean drainage that developed into a tunnel that eventually joined Cascade Creek farther downstream (2). (C) Eventually the tunnel collapsed, leaving a small remnant as Natural Bridge. Arrows show the direction of streamflow.

Believed to have been surveyed by George Washington in 1750 and owned by Thomas Jefferson in 1774, Natural Bridge is considered a unique natural wonder of the modern world.

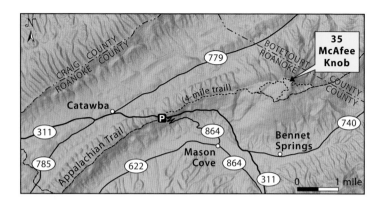

35 MCAFEE KNOB
A Suspended Slab of Tuscarora Sandstone
37° 22′ 48″ North, 80° 05′ 24″ West

Many seasoned hikers, having completed the Appalachian Trail from Springer Mountain, Georgia, to Mount Katahdin, Maine, agree that the most scenic spot along the 2,200-mile-long route lies atop the rounded Catawba Mountain, in Roanoke County. McAfee Knob, a 430-million-year-old, weathered, diving board–shaped slab of sandstone, is suspended precariously over a deep pool of air. At 3,197 feet, it offers hikers a commanding 270-degree panoramic view of Valley and Ridge terrain.

The 4-mile-long path to the top of the knob crisscrosses multiple outcrops harboring tidbits of geologic information useful for interpreting the early Paleozoic history of the surrounding countryside. The key formation of this narrative is the rock forming McAfee Knob itself, the Tuscarora Sandstone, composed almost entirely of quartz (aka silica dioxide). This very stable mineral remains chemically unaltered long after less-durable minerals are destroyed. Tuscarora samples collected within a 3-mile radius of McAfee Knob have an average 97.9 percent silica dioxide content.

The purity of the Tuscarora is evidence that its constituent grains underwent several cycles of erosion and deposition. Through each cycle the resulting sediment became increasingly quartz rich as less stable minerals were removed. Finally, during Early Silurian time—an age determined by studying the formations above and below the Tuscarora within the Commonwealth—the almost monomineralic sediment was compressed to form the Tuscarora Sandstone. During the Alleghanian Orogeny it was uplifted and folded in the cataclysm that created the Appalachian Mountains. Because this quartz-rich sedimentary rock is unusually resistant to erosion, it today forms many of the ridges that make up the Valley and Ridge Province.

Crossbedding and ripple marks are indications the Tuscarora was deposited in a nearshore marine environment. Tubelike features punctuating the sandstone are called scolithus, believed by paleontologists to have been formed by wormlike organisms that burrowed through the beach sand in search of food. The tubes later filled with sand and remain as fossil traces today.

Free from mineral impurities, domineering in appearance, and well known to generations of hikers, the lofty exposure of McAfee Knob is a scenic reminder of a multimillion-year span of geologic time involving repeated cycles of sediment cleansing.

Scolithus in a weathered boulder of Tuscarora Sandstone from McAfee Knob. The axial trace of a prominent burrow is front and center, and numerous circular, cross-sectional views are displayed on top. Pencil for scale.

Local legend has it that a beautiful redheaded woman periodically appears on McAfee Knob and beckons male visitors to join her in a leap to death. –Courtesy of Nathan Amick

SINKING CREEK MOUNTAIN

36

Massive Dip-Slope Landslide

37° 23' 13" North, 80° 13' 19" West

Mountain-building processes ended in the eastern United States around 260 million years ago, during Paleozoic time, when the compressional exertions of the Alleghanian Orogeny, the third and final episode in the growth of the Appalachian Mountains, were finally exhausted. Since then, the Himalayan heights of the youthful Appalachians have been reduced to the familiar rounded profiles seen throughout the Valley and Range Province of present-day Virginia. Wind and water have been the principal agents of erosion, but recent mapping in Montgomery and Giles Counties has identified an additional force—gravity.

Gargantuan, prehistoric landslides involving Silurian-age bedrock have been discovered along the southeast slopes of Sinking Creek Mountain, a 30-mile-long upland anticline

extending from Newport, in Giles County, northeast to New Castle, in Craig County. The zone of failure consists of seven or more slides distributed along a 20-mile-long sector centered to the northeast of the Caldwell Fields Campground, along County Road 621 in Montgomery County. The typical landslide block measures 1.7 miles long, 0.25 miles wide, and 80 to 300 feet thick and contains perhaps more than 17 billion cubic feet of rock. Downslope transportation distances range from 0.3 mile to a full mile. Prolonged weathering, erosion, and dissection have considerably reduced the original configuration of these displaced masses, leaving scattered remnants of formerly intact rock slabs.

The southeastern flank of Sinking Creek Mountain is a classic *dip slope*: a stretch of inclined land that is parallel or

An outstanding example of a Sinking Creek Mountain landslide block, as seen from County Road 621, in Craig County, about 16 miles east of the US 460 intersection. The linear evergreen growth zone (center background) identifies the top of the landslide mass. This Jefferson National Forest site is best viewed when the deciduous trees are bare.

subparallel to the dip of the underlying bedrock. For the most part, sandstone strata of the 250-foot-thick, 420-million-year-old Keefer Formation cover the entire dip slope of the mountain and dip (plunge) to the southeast from 25 to 65 degrees. Wherever this structural and topographic configuration is present, any number of triggering mechanisms might facilitate a gravity-driven landslide: pressure changes in rock and sediment related to rainfall, undercutting of the base of the dip slope by stream erosion, or ground vibration caused by earthquakes. With the latter potential trigger, such vibrations could originate from the nearby Giles County Seismic Zone, a 25-mile-long zone of moderate earthquake activity centered on the town of Pearisburg, west of Sinking Creek Mountain. This zone is the source of a 5.9 magnitude quake that rumbled across a 280,000-square-mile area in 1897.

Evidence indicates the Sinking Creek Mountain landslides were active 25,000 to 10,000 years ago, toward the end of the Ice Age but prior to the arrival of humans. There is no evidence of recent movement, but their reputation as the largest-known landslides in eastern North America—and among the largest in the world—suggests that perhaps their geologic moment of significance has not yet ended.

Extensive southeastern dipping exposures of Keefer Formation sandstone cover the southeastern flank of Sinking Creek Mountain, forming a dip-slope situation favorable to landsides.

Nearby Sinking Creek and a forest road are undercutting Silurian-age strata exposed along the base of Sinking Creek Mountain. This could jeopardize the stability of the sedimentary strata exposed farther up the mountain and initiate a new cycle of landslides.

37 DIXIE CAVERNS
Passage into Fort Lewis Mountain
37° 15′ 09″ North, 80° 10′ 30″ West

In the United States, it is very easy for us to take water for granted. It's a greatly undervalued convenience that we use in so many ways every day, from drinking it to bathing with it to washing our dishes and cars. Water is life—on average it makes up approximately 60 percent of the adult human body! It is definitely a win-win substance, and yet it has an unsavory side. In large volumes, water floods and destroys. As an atmospheric dervish, it forms the essence of hurricanes, and when it's pressurized in subterranean rock it induces earthquakes. Under the influence of acids it dissolves some types of rock, forming karst, a type of weathered landscape that covers 20 percent of the terrestrial surface of America.

Characterized by the presence of springs, caves, and sinkholes, karst, like water, also has opposing attributes. Sinkholes consume homes and lives, and karst-developed springs are commonly susceptible to contamination due to karst's porous nature. On the positive side, however, caverns are the delight of weekend spelunkers and summertime travelers seeking temperature-controlled, 57-degree relief from the heat. Dixie Caverns, in Roanoke County, is one of the better-known publicly accessible karst sites in the Old Dominion.

Visitors sometimes observe Dixie salamanders, a species unique to the Dixie Caverns, scampering among the folds of calcite formations, such as this curtain of stalactites.

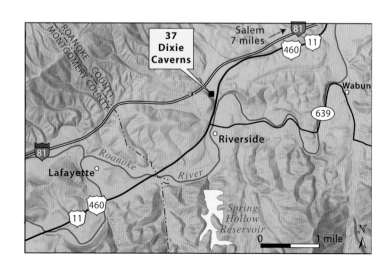

Discovered by a dog in 1920, Dixie Caverns is a perfect example that not all subterranean voids are created equal. Seemingly without fail, entering a commercially developed cavern is a down-down-down experience, but in this southwest Virginia locale it's an ascending exercise. Up, up, up you follow the forty-eight steps of Jacobs Ladder, through the south flank of Fort Lewis Mountain, and into the 160-foot-high splendor of the Cathedral Room.

Having formed recently in terms of geologic time, Dixie Caverns is still developing as acidic groundwater continues to dissolve 500-million-year-old Elbrook Formation dolomite. The ceiling and floor of the caverns are festooned with a myriad of stalactites and stalagmites, which form as groundwater and precipitation percolate downward and deposit calcium carbonate. Growing at about 1 cubic inch every 500 to 1,000 years, these calcite deposits constitute a fascinating collection of shapes denoted by whimsical names: Turkey Wing, Pipe Organ, and Wedding Bell. All are indefinitely entombed within a mountaintop depository of subterranean splendor.

Massive calcite deposits that span floor to ceiling are hauntingly reflected in the still waters of the Magic Mirror Room.
–© *Roanoke Times*, published with permission

38 MOUNTAIN LAKE
Mysterious Origins of a Temporary Pond
37° 21' 32" North, 80° 32' 05" West

Hired as a surveyor by the Ohio Company, an organization interested in settling territory beyond the Appalachian Mountains, Christopher Gist headed west, and on May 11, 1751, he discovered a "very high Mountain Lake or Pond . . . ¾ mile long . . . and ¼ mile wide." Seven years later settlers reported a grassy meadow at the same plot of elevated terrain they called Salt Pond Mountain. From these first contradictory recordings, Mountain Lake has continued to be a mysterious phenomenon in need of explanation.

Mountain Lake, in Giles County, has experienced desert-dry conditions at least six times: 4,200, 1,800, 1,200, 900, 400, and 100 years ago. Full in the year 2000 and empty in 2008, today it looks like a small pond. Several hypotheses have been advanced to explain its origins and mystifying water-level fluctuations.

Meteorite impact is the easiest idea to dismiss, due to the absence of a circular crater and any form of shocked quartz, both identifying features of high-velocity impact. Interpreting the lake basin as a sinkhole is also untenable because the local bedrock is composed entirely of sandstone and shale, non-carbonate-bearing strata that aren't susceptible to karst-type weathering.

Mass wasting, however, is an idea that has gained traction among geologists, and the presence of massive sharp-edged boulders along the north end of the Mountain Lake basin supports this hypothesis. Landslides triggered by seismic tremors could have created a rubble dam that would impound a stream, and numerous 4-to-5-magnitude earthquakes have been recorded in the Giles County Seismic Zone, a 25-mile-long sector of moderate earthquake activity centered on the town of Pearisburg, 10 miles due west of Mountain Lake (see also site 36). The inflow of sediment and organic litter could have sealed the rubble pile, giving rise to the formation of a lake. Subsequent earthquake activity, however, might have rearranged the inflow matter, in effect breaking the seal,

causing the lake level to drop. Repetition of this cycle might well explain the rise-and-fall-history of this mountain pond. In the late 1950s the lake level began to rise soon after an earthquake occurred that was strong enough to crack the mantle above the fireplace in the Mountain Lake hotel.

In short, mass wasting may well be the means and earthquakes the trigger for unraveling the geologic mystery and history of Mountain Lake, one of only two natural bodies of fresh water in the Old Dominion. (See site 2)

The high-and-dry boat dock (foreground), among other details, are indicative of recent declines in lake level. Massive angular blocks of Silurian-age sandstone, seen in the middle distance, support the theory that Mountain Lake was created by landslides triggered by earthquakes.

During the mid-2010s water depth at Mountain Lake was reduced from 100 feet to less than 15 feet, and a mere 15 percent of the basin was flooded. When the lake is at full stage the rock in the right foreground is submerged.

Aerial view, taken December 3, 2017, shows piles of landslide-related rock debris (upper right area) considered responsible for the formation of Mountain Lake, and the developing drainage system (lower central area) that is gradually refilling the lake. –Courtesy of Radford University Department of Geology

COAL MINING HERITAGE PARK
Underground Mine at Merrimac Ghost Town
37° 11' 22" North, 80° 25' 32" West

As far back as 1750 men and boys woke before the crack of dawn to begin their eight-to-ten-hour subterranean workday in an environment where the sun never shined. Originally mules removed token amounts of coal from the mines of central Virginia, but after industrial-scale machinery became commonplace production steadily rose in the years during and immediately after World War II. The large-scale extraction of coal from Montgomery County mines peaked at 200,000 tons in 1944 and ended in 1953, when the gates to the Big Vein mine were closed. Small and midsized family operations struggled on in central Virginia into the mid-1970s.

During the glory years of central Virginia coal production—the first four decades of the twentieth century—the mining of Virginia semianthracite was the chief source of nonagricultural income for the residents of Montgomery and Pulaski Counties. Hundreds of mines and prospects were active at a time when Mississippian-age coal—the oldest ever mined in the Old Dominion—was king, and hard work was an accepted way of life. In contrast to the bituminous Triassic-age coal of Virginia's eastern coalfields, and the bituminous Pennsylvanian-age product of the southwestern coalfields, the Mississippian-age coal of the valley coalfields is older semianthracite, a grade of coal with a high dollar value.

Coal is economically graded (or ranked) based on the process of coalification, the slow, natural means whereby buried plant material changes into ever denser, drier, more carbon-rich, and harder material. Lignite has the lowest rank because it contains a high percentage of volatile matter and a low level of carbon and produces high levels of air pollution. Bituminous, the most common type of coal used in electricity generation in the United States, has a middle rank, and anthracite, hard and brittle with a high percentage of carbon and a low percentage of volatile matter, has the highest rank.

At Coal Mining Heritage Park, shadows of this bygone era remain. Open dawn to dusk, the park is located at the base of Price Mountain, 3 miles southwest of Blacksburg. The 1.5-mile-long Loop Trail connects representative industrial elements—coal tipple, mine entrance, commissary, post office, hoist, and a typical coal car—of the mining town of Merrimac. This ghost of a once-thriving community functioned as a government colliery for the Confederacy and eventually became home to one of the largest mines in the district: the Merrimac Mine. Coal from this mine powered the *Merrimack*, the frigate that fought the *Monitor* in the Battle of Hampton Roads, the historic first engagement (March 8–9, 1862) between ironclad warships.

Over time, as the Merrimac operations became deeper, access to the coal beds became increasingly more difficult because the veins of coal were very steep and commonly broken: strata plunge into Price Mountain at angles of 23 to 45 degrees. The Merrimac Mine closed in 1935, the result of an extended labor dispute that marked the beginning of the end of a central Commonwealth industry and, now, an almost forgotten way of life.

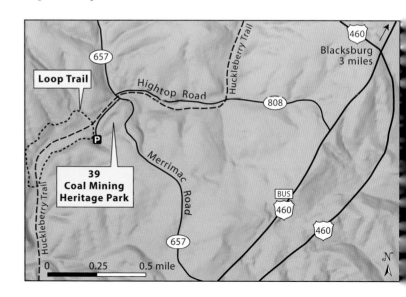

Coal cars like this remain sealed in the mine, subterranean evidence of a bygone era.

An exhaust pipe near the sealed entrance of the Merrimac Mine was used to keep the mine free of methane gas, a natural and often deadly by-product of coal production.

This steam-powered hoist pulled fully loaded, 1-ton coal cars out of the Merrimac Mine, a process key to the integrated operation that raised coal to the surface, where it was loaded into railroad cars and shipped to regions near and far.

The New River and the Narrows Water Gap as seen from downtown Narrows. The rapids at the heart of the gap lie just beyond the distant curve in the river. East River Mountain is on the left, Peters Mountain on the right. –Courtesy of Mack Gallimore

NARROWS WATER GAP
Ancient History of the New River
37° 20′ 54″ North, 80° 48′ 34″ West

Born in the highlands of western North Carolina, the New River flows northerly across the Blue Ridge Mountains, Valley and Ridge, and Appalachian Plateau before joining the drainage systems of the Ohio and Mississippi Rivers. A series of water gaps, each one a deep mountain gorge sculpted by water, marks its 360-mile course.

Narrows Water Gap, bookended by East River Mountain and Peters Mountain, is a 1,600-foot-deep chasm named after the nearby community of Narrows, in Giles County. It is a textbook example of a water gap, albeit one with an interesting history of investigation. The research has centered upon the age of the New River, how the water gap formed, and whether both age and process can be correlated with an antecedent or superimposed river genesis.

An *antecedent river* is one with a drainage established prior to mountain-building forces creating regional uplift. It is capable of maintaining its course and direction of flow by incising its channel at the same rate the land is elevated. A *superimposed river* develops its drainage differently: it develops on a young surface—composed perhaps of flat-lying sedimentary rocks—that overlies an old land surface with well-defined topography and maintains its course

Clinch Quartzite has the glazed appearance of a metamorphic rock. In actuality, this sandstone is so tightly cemented by silica that it's one of the most erosion-resistant sedimentary rocks found in the Appalachian Mountains. Quarter for scale.

Rapids formed by Silurian-age Clinch Quartzite cross the New River at the Narrows Water Gap. These strata plunge into the Earth at approximately 35 degrees, evidence of the intense tectonic forces that formed the Appalachian Mountains.

despite the different structures it encounters while eroding its channel downward. In the one case, the river comes first and stays put as structure forms beneath and around it. In the second case, the structure forms first, then a cover of rock is created, and finally the river forms and begins to etch through the covering surface and into the underlying structure.

Because no convincing evidence of a younger, covering surface of rock has been reported after more than two centuries of Appalachian Mountain field mapping, many geologists attribute the New River's development to the antecedent stream model. With this in mind, the river's relative age can be determined: because the Appalachian Mountains were last uplifted by tectonic forces of the Alleghanian Orogeny, during Pennsylvanian and Permian time, the New River and the Narrows Water Gap are at least 300 million years old. This Methuselah-type ancestry categorizes the New as the oldest watercourse on the North American continent. Only one question now remains: Why is the oldest river named the New River?

RADFORD UNIVERSITY MUSEUM OF THE EARTH SCIENCES
Exhilarating Exhibits about Life on Earth
37° 08′ 26″ North, 80° 33′ 02″ West

Across the length and breadth of Virginia there are numerous museums dedicated to the longest story ever told: the history of planet Earth. Some are expansive in size, some are small. Some are entertaining, some not so much. Some suffer from old age, some display the exuberance of youth. The Museum of the Earth Sciences is among the best. It's small in size but big in message, visually entertaining, brand-spanking new, and adorned with a wide range of "wow" factor stones-to-bones exhibits. Housed in the Center for the Sciences complex on the campus of Radford University, in Radford, it is designed to be an outreach museum encompassing the earth sciences of geology, meteorology, oceanography, paleontology, planetary astronomy, and physical anthropology.

Front and center at the museum entrance two life-size skulls are suspended in wide-mouthed killer-instinct poses: *Tyrannosaurus rex*, terrestrial giant of the Cretaceous world, and *Dunkleosteus*, marine tyrant of the Devonian world. Hollywood-style, 3D views of dinosaur life; a petrified remnant of the forest that shaded Virginia 100 million years ago; a reconstruction of the spiked, opportunistic trilobite predator *Terataspis*; and *Scyphocrinites*, the extinct sea lily that fed while floating upside down, are representative of a variety of free public exhibits.

Two displays are quite unique as far as museums go: a simulated underground passage highlighted by minerals that emit magical fluorescent radiance when activated by ultraviolet light, and a scale model of the Rock of Ages quarry—touted as the largest deep-hole granite excavation in the world—that for thirty years was on display at the Smithsonian Institute in Washington, DC.

Designed as a must-see destination, the Museum of the Earth Sciences is suggestive of the philosophy the famous Swiss geologist and glaciologist Louis Agassiz had in mind when encouraging his students to abandon the classroom in order to "study nature, not books."

Dunkleosteus *was possibly the largest animal to live until dinosaurs evolved. It lacked teeth and instead possessed long, bony, self-sharpening blades that sliced through flesh and crushed the bones of nearly anything that crossed its path.* –Courtesy of Radford University

This massive and thick skull of T. rex contains a mass of serrated teeth that served different functions: the front teeth grasped and pulled at the flesh making up a meal, those along the side tore the flesh free, and the ones in back diced the tidbits of raw meat and forced them into the throat. –Courtesy of Radford University

An armor of minute, bristly barbs protected the 2-foot-long Terataspis from predators. Paleontologists suspect it fed on decaying plants and animals. –Courtesy of Radford University

42 BURKES GARDEN
An Eroded Dome with a Sandstone Rim

37° 05′ 56″ North, 81° 20′ 29″ West

Tucked away in the Valley and Ridge Province of southwestern Virginia is a large rock-rimmed basin that has long been a topic of curiosity. Called Burkes Garden, or God's Thumbprint by some, this oval bowl of sedimentary rock is the highest mountain valley in Virginia. About 8 miles long and 4 miles wide, Burkes Garden appears as out of place in the mountainous terrain of Tazewell County as would an oval-shaped NFL stadium in the middle of a large cornfield. It's unusual and perhaps even unique, but what caused it?

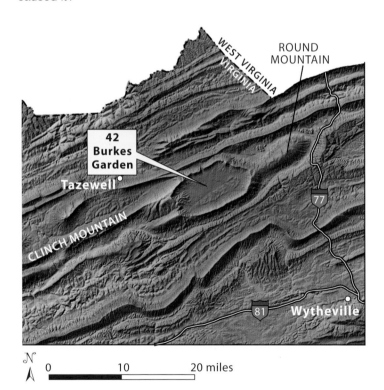

Burkes Garden (center) stands out on this three-dimensional shaded relief map. Its long axis parallels the axis of both Clinch Mountain (lower left) and Round Mountain (center right).

From the vantage point of an airplane, this geologic structure might appear to be the crater left by a gargantuan meteorite that collided with Earth. However, the energy produced by an impacting celestial object commonly blankets the countryside with a debris field containing the rare element iridium and creates a wall-of-fire conflagration that engulfs the immediate area. Evidence for either of these smoking guns has not been found.

Some wondered if Burkes Garden might be the topographic expression of an ancient lake that fell victim to global warming. To scientifically support such an idea, fossil remains of freshwater life would need to be found. Fossils are found here—*Arthrophycus*, a trace fossil thought to have been formed by a trilobite, and *Orospira*, a genus of gastropod (snail)—but they are embedded in sandstone and limestone that were deposited in a shallow, saltwater ocean millions of years ago. So scratch that hypothesis. Finally, the idea of Burkes Garden as a volcanic crater is untenable because volcanic activity is associated with igneous rocks, formed from cooled magma. Within the immediate area such rocks are conspicuously absent.

The geologic history of Burkes Garden can be traced back some 500 million years, to when layers of sediment were deposited and compressed into rock. Much later—during the Alleghanian Orogeny—they were folded into an elongate dome. Over time, the hard roof of Silurian-age Clinch Quartzite eroded away, exposing the underlying, soluble Ordovician-age Beekmantown Dolomite that today shapes the valley floor. Remnants of the resistant Clinch Quartzite form the unbroken wall of Garden Mountain that defines the outline of the breached dome.

BURKES GARDEN DOME

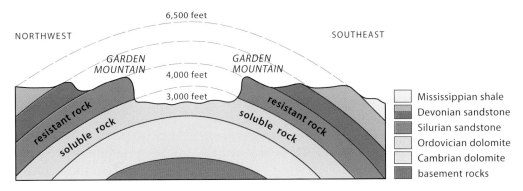

Simplified geologic cross section across Burkes Garden. It is estimated that the original dome (dashed lines) was 6,500 feet in elevation before erosion created the 3,000-foot-high, oval-shaped valley (center) rimmed by Garden Mountain.

NORTHWEST   SOUTHEAST

6,500 feet

GARDEN MOUNTAIN   GARDEN MOUNTAIN

4,000 feet

3,000 feet

resistant rock   resistant rock

soluble rock   soluble rock

Mississippian shale
Devonian sandstone
Silurian sandstone
Ordovician dolomite
Cambrian dolomite
basement rocks

Looking to the west-southwest, the view overlooks the oval outline of Burkes Garden, highlighted by autumn colors.
–Courtesy of Grubb Photo Service

103

MUSEUM OF THE MIDDLE APPALACHIANS
Salt, the Essence of Life and Preservation
36° 52' 48" North, 81° 45' 50" West

Tucked away in the southwest environs of the Valley and Ridge Province, the little mountain town of Saltville, in Smyth County, has a 350-million-year-long story to tell linked by a common theme: salt. This chronicle includes aspects of geology, paleontology, archeology, and modern-day commerce. Shallow ponds immediately south of the community serve as testimony to events of deep-time mountain building, Ice Age life, Native American cultures, Civil War armies, and the modern world.

During the Mississippian Period, salt layers of the Maccrady Formation were deposited in a tidal-flat environment when Virginia and much of the eastern seaboard were inundated by the Panthalassa Ocean. The salt was later folded and faulted during the final stages of the development of the Appalachian Mountains, during Permian time. These once horizontal and laterally continuous beds of sodium chloride were transformed into isolated and fragmented segments, a condition that makes subsurface mining impractical. Over time, groundwater circulating through these disseminated pods of evaporites emerged at the surface in the form of *licks*, springs enriched in salt.

Toward the end of the Ice Age, 14,000 years ago, hordes of large mammals were attracted to the aroma of the saline marshlands. Inevitably some animals were trapped in the soggy ground, and their skeletons were entombed within oxygen-deficient soils. Since the late 1700s, excavations

Mammoth teeth are composed of a series of rubberband-shaped enamel plates that formed a grinding surface well adapted for dining on tough grasses, a favorite food of these grassland herbivores. Pen for scale. –Courtesy of Janice Orr, Museum of the Middle Appalachians

Today brine wells and evaporating towers in Saltville produce pinhead-sized cubes of sodium chloride that is 99.7 percent pure.

Paleontological digs along the Helen Williams Barbrow Interpretive Trail are reminiscent of the soggy conditions that entrapped now-extinct Ice Age mammals 14,000 years ago.

have yielded a treasure trove of vertebrate remains: musk oxen, giant ground sloths, moose, caribou, and woolly mammoths and mastodons—the latter the favorites of many fossil enthusiasts.

At least twenty Native American village sites have been found in the vicinity of Saltville, an indication that these communities treasured salt as a food preservative and seasoning. During the Civil War the town became the salt capital of the Confederacy when access to other southern sources was lost to Union forces: in 1864, 4 million bushels were produced in Saltville, two-thirds of all the salt required annually by the Confederacy.

Today, snow-white salt is produced several miles southwest of Saltville. Brine water extracted from wells drilled into the salt layers collects in large-scale evaporating towers. The resulting salt is sold as a deicer, a water softener, and iodized table salt. Every aspect of this rich and extended cavalcade of scientific and social history is on daily exhibit at the Museum of the Middle Appalachians, on Palmer Avenue in Saltville.

44 GREAT CHANNELS
Sandstone Labyrinth on Clinch Mountain
36° 51' 52" North, 81° 56' 49" West

Concealed in an alpine-like setting, crafted from 430-million-year-old Clinch Quartzite, and characterized by 40-to-50-foot-deep fractures, there lies a labyrinth of moss-covered channels immediately outside the small town of Hayters Gap, in Washington County. Known as the Great Channels, they compose one of the most unusual rock locales found anywhere in the Appalachian Mountains. The quartz-rich Silurian-age Clinch contains crossbeds, ripple marks, and the trace fossil *Arthrophycus*—casts of worm borings made in beach sands—suggesting the rock was deposited in a nearshore, aquatic environment.

Travelers captivated by the beauty and form of the semi-claustrophobic red-rock topography of southeast Utah may feel right at home in the white-to-gray rock scenery of the Great Channels, located at the end of the Brumley Mountain Trail, 3 miles off VA 80. The sandstone in both these areas has been sculpted into *slot canyons*, narrow, bare-rock crevices that deepen into sheer-walled foyers swathed in semidarkness. The slot canyons of Utah formed when the destructive agents of erosion (wind, water, and ice) infiltrated hairline rock fractures, eroding and widening the cracks. Flash floods invaded the passageways, as well, plucking out rock fragments and deepening the channels. Over time the slots grew in grandeur and depth.

In the case of the Great Channels, called "wind tunnels" by local residents, neither air currents nor flash flooding played a role in their development. Field studies suggest they were created under the influence of the periglacial conditions that enveloped Virginia during the Pleistocene Epoch. While continental ice sheets only reached as far south as the Ohio River, arctic-like conditions beyond the margins of the ice invaded the rocky crest of Clinch Mountain, where the slots are located. Freezing and thawing expanded existing bedrock fractures, wedging them open and leaving broken, steep-walled chasms.

Only recently accessible to the public, the Great Channels is still a well-kept secret. First-time visitors who venture to the 4,208-foot-high crest of Clinch Mountain and discover this rhododendron-and-blueberry-thicket-covered panorama of rock and erosion generally have but one word to describe their experience: "exhilarating."

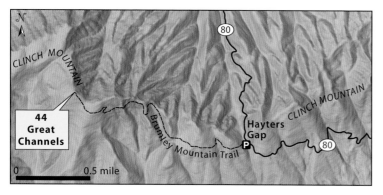

Once thought to be the remains of a prehistoric plant, these simple, rounded ridges are now known as Arthrophycus, a trace fossil of overlapping and intersecting worm burrows. Penny for scale.

Moss covered and continually damp, this Great Channels slot canyon narrows to an escape (center) that even a child might approach with caution. –Courtesy of Nathan Amick

Concealed by a verdant coating of vegetation, fractured Clinch Quartzite lies partially exposed along the crest of Clinch Mountain. –Courtesy of Nathan Amick

45 SINKHOLE VALLEY
Groundbreaking Phenomena of Subterranean Significance

36° 57' 30" North, 82° 09' 44" West

Sinkholes can create nightmarish situations. Born without warning, they can consume automobiles, homes, parking lots, and even neighborhood baseball fields. Statistics compiled by the US Geological Survey show that as much as 20 percent of the landscape in the United States is susceptible to sinkhole development. In Virginia more than 49,000 sinkholes pockmark the twenty-nine counties of the Valley and Ridge Province.

Rock-consuming groundwater, derived from acidic rainwater and enhanced by contact with acid-bearing organic soils, slowly dissolves carbonate bedrock, such as limestone and dolomite, leaving a subterranean system of fissures, caves, and caverns. This combination of soluble rock and acidic groundwater commonly results in a style of topography known as karst. Bowl or funnel shaped, often with vertical sides, *sinkholes* are depressions in the surface of karst. They form when the roofs of underground voids collapse. Occasionally, karst develops to the extent that chains of sinkholes coalesce to form elongated, low-lying landscapes known as solution valleys. Sinkhole Valley, in Russell County, is a textbook example of one of these.

Confined by County Roads 616 (to the west), 615 (to the north), and 663 (to the east), and anchored to the south by the community of Cleveland, Sinkhole Valley is an undulating, 6-square-mile rectangle of land. It overlies bedrock composed of 340-million-year-old Greenbrier Limestone, which was deposited in a shallow marine environment similar to that of the modern-day Bahamas. More than fifty sinkholes puncture this valley. Some are small and considered mere inconveniences. Others—proof that size does indeed matter—are capable of destroying life and infrastructure. A prime example is the home-sized sinkhole observed from the berm of County Road 725, 0.5 mile west of its intersection with VA 600. With approximately 150 feet of relief and floored with a pond situated 1,854 feet above sea level, this depression marks the local upper level of acidic groundwater, the limestone-dissolving culprit that continues to reshape the karst topography of Sinkhole Valley.

The central part of Sinkhole Valley, north of Cleveland, showing access to the two views (A and B) seen in the accompanying photographs. Sinkholes are brown, and sinkhole ponds are blue.

Ripple marks in the Greenbrier Limestone (location B on the accompanying map) were created by currents or by the agitation of water by waves in an aquatic environment. Pen for scale.

Large enough to completely engulf the nearby 60-foot-long home, this 82-foot-diameter pond occupies a 500-foot-diameter sinkhole off the berm of County Route 725 (location A on the accompanying map).

46 NATURAL TUNNEL STATE PARK
Collaboration between a Sinkhole and a Fault
36° 42' 08" North, 82° 44' 46" West

About 450 million years ago the land that would become Virginia was located several degrees south of the equator, inundated by an inland sea. Invertebrate organisms, such as trilobites, brachiopods, gastropods, and pelecypods abounded in the tepid waters. Over time the shells of these aquatic animals accumulated on the seafloor and were slowly

compacted into a 2,000-foot-thick mass of carbonate rock that is subdivided into three Ordovician-age formations: the Chepultepec limestone, Longview dolomite and limestone, and the Kingsport dolomite and limestone.

Fast-forward to the Permian Period, 175 million years after the limy sediments were first deposited. Energized by the dynamics of plate tectonics, the continents of Earth were involved in a clash of landmasses that climaxed with the birth of the Appalachian Mountains. The limestone and dolomite strata of southwest Virginia were folded and faulted, setting the stage for the development of the 900-foot-long Natural Tunnel, in the state park of the same name in Duffield, in Scott County.

After millions of years of wind, water, and ice erosion, a sinkhole began to form in the carbonate bedrock of Scott County some 850,000 years ago. It diverted Stock Creek underground and directed it along the trace of Glenita Fault, a zone of rock fracturing and movement created by compressional forces during the building of the Appalachian Mountains in Permian time. Eventually Stock Creek surfaced as a large spring. Today the sinkhole is the North Portal at the park, and the spring the South Portal, the back and front doors of Natural Tunnel, respectively.

The ten-story-high arched massif that accentuates Natural Tunnel State Park is a marvel to behold. Crafted by rock dissolution over hundreds of thousands of years, the story of this feature continues today, as humans have left their own indelible mark. It is perforated by a coal-carrying rail line and crowned by a highway, neither of which detract from its magnificence. Perhaps the largest tunnel in the world formed by the dissolution of carbonate rock, noted American orator and politician William Jennings Bryan designated it the "eighth wonder of the world."

The South Portal entrance to Natural Tunnel showing the rail line (center), with Stock Creek to the left. In general the tunnel is 175 feet wide and 80 feet high.
—Courtesy of the Virginia Department of Conservation and Recreation

Glenita Fault, the zone of fragmented rock that, along with a sinkhole, helped create Natural Tunnel, crosses the South Portal wall. Movement along the fault (shown by arrows) bent underlying strata upward.

UNDEFORMED STRATA

GLENITA FAULT

DEFORMED STRATA

A chairlift bypasses the steep, 0.3-mile-long cliffside trail to South Portal, the front door of Natural Tunnel.

47 MILLBRIG ASHFALL
An Ordovician Supervolcano
36° 41′ 58″ North, 83° 17′ 16″ West

Approximately 1,500 active volcanoes mottle Earth's surface—the acne of its terrestrial complexion. Of the roughly 500 that have erupted within recorded history, more than half define the Ring of Fire, the chain of volcanism that follows the periphery of the Pacific Ocean. Many of these have displayed Vesuvian characteristics: violent explosions of viscous, gas-filled lava accompanied by large volumes of fine-grained ash.

Mount St. Helens erupted for a full nine hours. Following the 1991 eruption of Pinatubo, in the Philippine Islands, average global temperatures declined a full 1 degree Fahrenheit. The explosion of Vesuvius in AD 79 killed an estimated 10,000 to 25,000 people and completely buried the cities of Pompeii and Herculaneum. Heard fully 3,000 miles away,

the 1883 explosion of Krakatoa in Indonesia activated barographs (used to measure barometric pressure) around the world. The volume of ash Tambora blew into the Indonesian atmosphere in 1815 created a worldwide famine.

These volcanic behemoths are impressive in scope and for their destructive power, but their reputations are reduced when compared to the eruptive event that occurred when the island arc Taconica collided with ancestral North America. Of the more than sixty known volcanic ash beds that resulted from this Late Ordovician event, one possesses impressive credentials: the 3-to-6.5-foot-thick, 454-million-year-old Millbrig bentonite bed was deposited across an area that stretched from Vermont to Nebraska and Mississippi northward into Ontario.

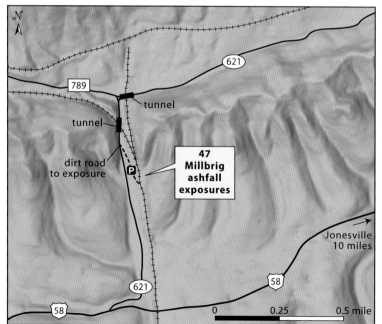

In spite of its age, the rust-colored, wind-deposited Millbrig ash is only semiconsolidated, whereas the enveloping gray limestone has been solid rock for millions of years. Pencil for scale.

A beautiful exposure of Millbrig ash is part of a hillside abutting railroad tracks in a remote part of Lee County. Travel 10 miles west of Jonesville on US 58 and turn north on VA 621 (Burning Well Road). Drive 0.7 mile to a rough dirt road exiting on the right. Drive or walk up the road for 0.15 mile to a 3-to-5-vehicle parking area. The ash exposure is 60 yards to the right along the railroad tracks.

The Millbrig ash bed increases in thickness to the south and west. Because a larger amount of ash would have settled to the ground closer to the volcano, this configuration suggests the parent volcano was sited in the general vicinity of present-day Tennessee, in an area then inundated by the Iapetus Ocean. The explosion of this unnamed supervolcano belched more than 270 cubic miles of ash into the atmosphere, more than 400 times the volume of ash associated with the catastrophic 1980 eruption of Mount St. Helens.

Bookended by gray-toned beds of limestone, this blushing-red band of semiconsolidated rock attained super-star status when it was declared evidence of possibly the largest-known eruption to have occurred in the eastern United States during the last 500 million years. A new chapter in geologic—as well as human—history would be necessary should an eruption of this intensity ever occur again.

Ordovician-age limestone, deposited in the warm waters of the Iapetus Ocean, envelop the 3-to-6.5-foot-thick Millbrig ash (red exposure) in Lee County.

48 CUMBERLAND GAP
The Way West by Fault and Crater
36° 36' 10" North, 83° 41' 46" West

Early eighteenth-century migration beyond the Blue Ridge Mountains was hindered by elevated topography that filled the western horizon. For a long time, well-worn bison and Native American trails were the only way over the forested ridges that crossed the landscape like wrinkles in a rug. The Cumberland Gap, discovered in 1750 by Virginia physician and explorer Dr. Thomas Walker, however, provided a practical route, and soon families in Conestoga wagons were wending their way through the mountains via this low-level passage. Daniel Boone crossed the gap in 1775 and made it part of the much larger Wilderness Road that allowed settlers to reach the land he called "Kaintuck." To understand the genesis of the gap, we need to go back further in time.

The geographic scene of Paleozoic time was characterized by the to-and-fro meanderings of eight major landmasses that slowly coalesced as the supercontinent Pangaea. The climax of this tectonic dance—the Alleghanian Orogeny—resulted in the Appalachian Mountains and the creation of Cumberland Mountain, which separates Virginia from Kentucky. Constructed of a 130-mile-long mass of folded Paleozoic-age sedimentary rock, Cumberland Mountain is weakened by several crosscutting fractures.

One of these fractures—the steeply dipping, north-south-oriented Rocky Face Fault—is responsible for the location of Cumberland Gap. The linear zone of shattered and fragmented rock created by movement along the fault became the course of a river—perhaps the headwaters of the ancestral Cumberland River. In time this river eroded its way through the fractured rock, creating a 4,600-foot-long, 600-to-900-foot-deep water gap.

In 1966 an astrobleme was discovered, adding another chapter to the history of the gap. Some 300 million years ago, a meteorite approximately the size of a football field impacted the region, creating a 3.7-mile-diameter crater, today remaining as an ancient, circular erosional scar that has minimal surface expression. Rock and mineral analysis revealed the presence of shatter cones and shocked quartz, rock features that only form under extremely high pressure and temperature conditions. Ground zero is located on the grounds of the Middlesboro Country Club, about 5 miles west of the gap. The energy associated with this impact further enhanced the physical dimensions of the nearby gap by removing fragmented debris along the Rocky Face Fault.

Today Cumberland Gap is a *wind gap*—an abandoned water gap best viewed from the heights of the Cumberland Mountains at Pinnacle Overlook. It was born of multiple geologic processes over millions of years, and it eventually opened the proverbial door to the West a mere twenty-seven decades ago.

PINNACLE OVERLOOK

Cumberland Gap, as seen from US 58, 0.25 mile east of the intersection with US 25E. Pinnacle Overlook (small white exposure of rock) is visible on the right flank, 0.75 mile up the slope.

Shatter cones in Paleozoic-age bedrock exposed at Middlesboro Country Club. These linear structures are created by shock waves generated during a meteorite impact. Quarter for scale.

An exposure of the trace of the Rocky Face Fault. This fractured rock is in the parking lot of the Fort McCook Civil War earthworks, along the winding Pinnacle View Road to Pinnacle Overlook, on the northeast flank of Cumberland Gap.

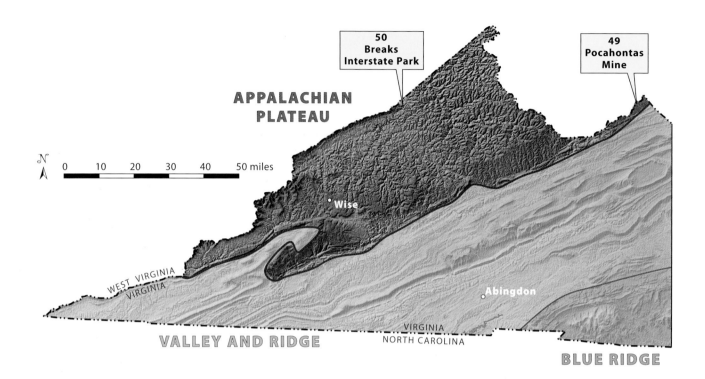

APPALACHIAN PLATEAU

Located in the extreme southwestern part of the state, the Appalachian Plateau Province is the smallest of Virginia's five physiographic regions. Spread across a three-county area, it is an elevated area that has been strongly dissected by well-established streams and rivers. Bedrock is principally late Paleozoic in age, and because of its overall flat-lying nature the different formations can be easily correlated from outcrop to outcrop. The plateau's regional-scale folding was caused by the compressional forces that created the Appalachian Mountains.

More than 20,000 feet of sedimentary rock underlie the Appalachian Plateau, and the upper reaches are rich in mineral resources, including limestone, petroleum, natural gas, and several grades of coal, the latter having formed some 300 million years ago during the Pennsylvanian Period. Extraction of these resources has long played, and continues to play, a significant role in the human and economic history of the region.

POCAHONTAS MINE
No. 3 Coal, America's Most Highly Regarded Fuel

37° 18′ 27″ North, 81° 20′ 46″ West

During the course of two world wars, No. 3 coal from Pocahontas Mine No. 1 was the fuel of choice for the US Navy—and for good reason. When properly fired its "smokeless" quality allowed ships to remain unnoticed by the enemy from a distance. Opened to production in 1882 and marketed under the name OP—Original Pocahontas—the readily combustible rock that forms the No. 3 coal seam would become one of America's most highly regarded fuels for its distinctive qualities: a low (0.5–0.8 percent) sulfur content,

a high carbon content, its value in the making of coke for use in steelmaking, and high *heating value*—a measure of the amount of heat released by burning a specified volume. With a maximum thickness of 13 feet, the No. 3 seam is the thickest of nine coal beds, numbered from the bottom up, that occur in the Pennsylvanian-age Lee Formation in southwestern Virginia. In short, No. 3 coal was a valuable sedimentary rock that burns clean and, an added advantage, could be produced by miners working upright rather than on the hands-and-knees position common to many underground operations.

Roughly 300 million years ago, during the Carboniferous Period, large portions of the eastern United States were covered by wetlands that extended from Alabama into northern Pennsylvania. These humongous swamps were covered by layers of woody vegetation that, over time, created deep organic-rich layers. During the Alleghanian Orogeny, the third and final phase of mountain building instrumental in the development of the Appalachian Mountains, these layers were uplifted. Varying degrees of tectonic pressure and temperature compacted and altered the unconsolidated deposits of organic residue into four major types (or ranks) of coal: from lowest to highest, lignite, subbituminous, bituminous, and anthracite. Each is defined by characteristic chemical and physical qualities. Pocahontas No. 3 coal is classed as bituminous in rank; it's relatively soft, dark brown to black in color, and 60 to 80 percent carbon with the remaining content being water, air, hydrogen, and sulfur.

In southwestern Virginia the thickest example of No. 3 coal is exposed in Tazewell County near Pocahontas, Virginia's first coalfield boomtown and home to historic Pocahontas Mine No. 1, the initial operation to exploit the rich seams of the Pocahontas Coalfield. Covering 30 square miles, the Pocahontas Mine No. 1 operated for 73 years and produced some 44 million tons of No. 3 coal, enough to fill a train 6,000 miles long.

OP coal from the No. 3 seam, artistically advertised by this porcelain sign, is still rated as some of the best coal to be found in the world.

Mine No. 1 has yielded many plant fossils typical of the Carboniferous-age swamps of the eastern United States. This example contains a beautifully preserved fern branch and a mishmash of related plant material. Lens cap for scale.

An 8-foot-long bolt keeps this Mine No. 1 kettle bottom from falling and killing an unsuspecting worker, a common occurrence in southwestern Virginia coal mines.

Located next to Mine No. 1, on the northwest edge of the community of Pocahontas, this 8-foot-thick roadside exposure of No. 3 coal is 5 feet shy of the maximum 13-foot-thickness found in nearby exposures.

A visit to the Pocahontas Exhibition Coal Mine and Museum is a unique opportunity to return to that era when coal was king, America ran on steam power, and there was a chicken in the pot for every coal-mining family on Sunday. Seasonal underground tours led by retired miners highlight the carbonaceous outlines of fossil fish; a section of fossil bark characteristic of the vegetation that thrived in the long-ago murky conditions that ultimately created No. 3 coal; and a prime example of a "kettle bottom," miners' jargon for a mud-formed replica of a fossil root or tree trunk that extends upward into the roof of a coal seam. These fossil kettle bottoms were responsible for making many "coal widows" when they broke loose and killed unsuspecting miners.

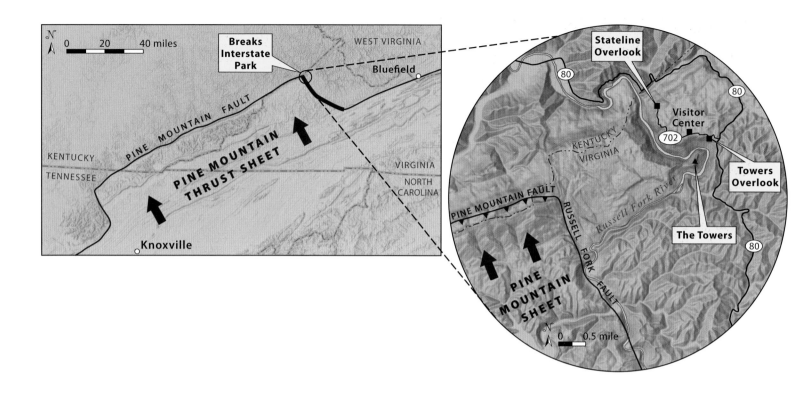

![Map showing Breaks Interstate Park location with Pine Mountain Thrust Sheet and detailed inset of the park area]

50 BREAKS INTERSTATE PARK
Grand Canyon of the South
37° 17' 13" North, 82° 17' 46" West

When ancestral North America and ancestral Africa collided in a continental-crunching collision at the end of the Paleozoic Era, the topographic profile of North America took on a Himalayan-like character that prevailed for millions of years. Sedimentary rocks along the eastern seaboard rippled and folded upward into cloud-piercing mountains and then ruptured in the form of massive thrust sheets. These sheets, each composed of one large block of Earth's crust, were driven up and over each other until they resembled shingles layered on a roof. One such rectangular block of rock—the Pine Mountain Thrust Sheet—occupies a large swath of southwestern Virginia.

Oriented northeast to southwest, the Pine Mountain Thrust Sheet is the northernmost expression of the Appalachian Plateau Province in the Commonwealth. During the Alleghanian Orogeny, the final tectonic episode that created the Appalachian Mountains, this massive slab of rock—125 miles long, 25 miles wide, and up to 2 miles thick—was tectonically bulldozed to the northwest more than 12 miles from its original location. Today it is bounded to the northwest by the Pine Mountain Fault, and to the northeast by the Russell Fork Fault. One cannot see the entire thrust sheet in all its glory from any one place, but several vistas in Breaks Interstate Park, in extreme northeastern Dickenson County, offer glimpses.

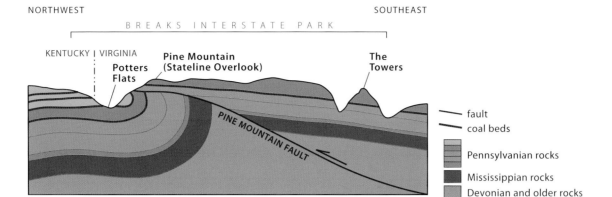

NORTHWEST   SOUTHEAST

BREAKS INTERSTATE PARK

KENTUCKY | VIRGINIA

Potters   Pine Mountain   The
Flats   (Stateline Overlook)   Towers

PINE MOUNTAIN FAULT

fault
coal beds
Pennsylvanian rocks
Mississippian rocks
Devonian and older rocks

0.25 mile

Cross section through Breaks Interstate Park showing the leading edge of the Pine Mountain Thrust Sheet (area above the Pine Mountain Fault). The thrust sheet was forced to the northwest along the Pine Mountain Fault, up and over Mississippian- and Pennsylvanian-age strata folded by this movement. As a result, deeply buried rocks were exposed at the surface.

View across Potters Flats into Kentucky from the Stateline Overlook. Beds of Pennsylvanian-age coal are exposed in the distant forested riverbank of the Russell Fork.

Stateline Overlook is located on the crest of Pine Mountain, immediately east of the Russell Fork Fault. It was along this fault that the Pine Mountain Thrust Sheet moved 12 miles. The Towers, seen from the Towers Overlook, are two cliff-lined erosional palisades of Pennsylvanian-age Bee Rock Sandstone embraced by a giant meander of the Russell Fork.

The channel of this north-flowing river closely follows a linear zone of fractured and broken blocks of sandstone that marks the trace of the Russell Fork Fault. River erosion along the fault trace has carved a 5-mile-long, 1,650-foot-deep gorge, aptly named the Grand Canyon of the South and renowned as the largest gorge east of the Mississippi River.

Viewed from the Towers Overlook, the Towers is capped by a column of crossbedded Bee Rock Sandstone (upper center) deposited 300 million years ago, when a vast inland sea covered this part of Virginia and Kentucky.

GLOSSARY

Acadian Orogeny. The second of three phases of mountain building that were instrumental in the development of the Appalachian Mountains during the Paleozoic Era.

algae. Primitive aquatic plants that lack true stems, roots, and leaves.

Alleghanian Orogeny. The third of three phases of mountain building that were instrumental in the development of the Appalachian Mountains during the Paleozoic Era.

amniotic egg. An egg produced by reptiles, birds, and egg-laying mammals in which the embryo develops inside a membranous sac.

amphibian. Any vertebrate that breathes with gills in the early stages of life and with lungs in the later stages.

anhydrite. A mineral composed of anhydrous (no water) calcium carbonate.

anthracite. Hard, black coal of the highest metamorphic rank that burns with a blue flame and without smoke.

anticline. A convex-upward fold with a core that contains stratigraphically older rocks.

ashfall. Airborne ash that falls from an eruption cloud, and the resulting deposit.

asteroid. One of many small celestial bodies in orbit around the Sun.

asthenosphere. The layer of the Earth below the lithosphere in which isostatic adjustments take place.

basalt. A general term for dark-colored mafic igneous rocks.

basement. The undifferentiated complex of typically crystalline rocks underlying the sedimentary deposits in a region.

basin. A depressed area with no surface outlet for water.

bed. The smallest sedimentary unit that is distinguishable from those above and below it based on sediment type, size, and/or color.

bedding plane. The surface of separation between any two distinct beds of sedimentary rock.

bedrock. A general term for rock, usually solid, that underlies soil or other unconsolidated, superficial material.

bentonite. A soft, porous rock composed of clay minerals produced by the chemical alteration of a glassy igneous material, usually tuff or volcanic ash.

biomass. The amount of living material in a particular area, stated in terms of the weight or volume of organisms per unit area.

bituminous coal. A dark-brown to black variety of coal that burns with a smoky flame and is the most abundant type of coal in the United States.

blastoid. An extinct class of marine animals that is related to modern-day starfish and sea lilies. Often called sea buds, the fossils look like hickory nuts.

bolide. An exploding or exploded meteor or meteoroid.

boulder field. An accumulation of usually angular blocks on top of solid or weathered bedrock that lacks an apparent source, such as a cliff above.

brachiopod. A marine invertebrate with bivalve shells enclosing arm structures used to sweep food into the mouth. Also called a lampshell.

bryozoan. A small aquatic invertebrate that feeds with a crown of hollow tentacles, has a calcareous skeleton, and forms colonies. Also called a moss animal.

calcareous. Consisting of calcium carbonate.

calcium carbonate. A compound composed of calcium, carbon, and oxygen that is found in nature as the minerals aragonite and calcite in bones and shells.

carbonate. A mineral, such as calcite or aragonite, containing a carbonate ion. Also a sedimentary rock, such a limestone, chalk, or dolostone, composed of appreciable amounts of carbonate minerals.

cephalopod. A marine organism with an internal shell, such as an octopus or nautilus.

chert. A hard, extremely dense microcrystalline sedimentary rock consisting dominantly of interlocking crystals of quartz.

columnar jointing. Parallel, prismatic columns, polygonal in cross section, found in basaltic flows and caused by contraction during cooling.

conglomerate. A sedimentary rock composed of rounded pebbles, cobbles, and boulders held together by a fine-grained matrix of sediment or natural cement.

continental shelf. A shallow submarine plain along the edge of a continent that typically ends with a steep drop to the deep ocean.

coral. A general name for a large group of bottom-dwelling invertebrate organisms common in warm seas. They typically live in colonies; some species form reefs.

core. The central zone of the Earth's interior below a depth of 1,800 miles. It is composed of an inner, solid subcore and an outer, fluid subcore.

crater. A rimmed basin-like structure that is usually at the summit of a volcanic cone.

crinoid. A marine animal characterized by a cup-shaped body, feathery arms, and a clawlike stem attached to the seafloor. Also known as a sea lily or feather-star.

crossbed. A sedimentary rock layer inclined at an angle to the main planes of stratification.

crust. Earth's outermost shell, which varies in thickness between 6 and 25 miles.

diabase. An intrusive rock whose main minerals are labradorite and pyroxene.

differential weathering. Weathering that occurs at different rates because of variations in the composition and resistance of a rock or group of rocks.

dike. A tabular igneous intrusion that cuts across the bedding or foliation of the country rock.

diorite. A gray to dark-gray plutonic rock consisting principally of the minerals plagioclase, feldspar, and hornblende.

dissolution. The dissolving of rock by chemical processes.

dolomite. A carbonate sedimentary rock in which more than 50 percent by weight consists of the mineral dolomite.

dropstone. An oversized stone (relative to surrounding sediment) in layered sediment that depresses the underlying layer. Generally deposited as a result of the melting of its host ice.

erosion. The general process whereby the materials of the Earth's crust are loosened, dissolved, or worn away and simultaneously moved from one place to another by natural forces, such as water, wind, ice, and gravity.

escarpment. A long continuous cliff separating two sloping surfaces that is the product of erosion or faulting.

exoskeleton. A supportive and protective framework that lies outside the body tissues of an animal, forming an external armor.

fall line. An imaginary line connecting the waterfalls on adjacent, relatively parallel rivers that marks the point where the rivers make a sudden descent from an upland to a lowland. In the eastern United States, the Fall Line marks the upper limits of navigation.

fault. A fracture along which rock on one side has moved relative to rock on the other side.

fauna. The entire animal population, living or fossil, of a given area, environment, or time span.

flood basalt. Flows of basalt lava that flooded Earth's surface on a regional scale.

flora. The entire plant population, living or fossil, of a given area, environment, or time span.

flowstone. A general term for any calcium carbonate deposit formed by water flowing on the walls or floor of a cave.

foliation. The planar arrangement of textural or structural features in any type of rock.

formation. The basic cartographic rock unit in geologic mapping. A formation has easily recognized boundaries, based on its rock characteristics, that can be traced along an outcrop in the field and in the subsurface.

fossil. The remains or evidence of preexisting life.

gastropod. An organism with a coiled shell, such as a snail, slug, or limpet.

genus. A unique group of organisms with one common characteristic or several common characteristics.

glacier. A mass of ice that moves outward in all directions due to gravity and the force of its own weight.

gneiss. A foliated rock formed by regional metamorphism and characterized by alternating light and dark bands of flaky minerals.

Gondwanaland. The late Precambrian to late Paleozoic continent of the southern hemisphere and counterpart to Laurentia in the northern hemisphere that was the precursor of Africa.

graben. An elongate trough bounded on both sides by high-angle normal faults that dip toward the interior of the trough.

granite. A coarse-grained, light-colored igneous rock, rich in quartz and potassium feldspar, that formed from magma that cooled and crystallized below the surface.

granodiorite. A rock that is similar to granite that contains more plagioclase feldspar than orthoclase feldspar and a quartz content greater than 20 percent by volume. It is gray in color.

Grenville Mountains. The mountain range, formed by the collision of several microcontinents late in Precambrian time, that is the geologic core of eastern North America.

groundwater. A general term for all subsurface water, as distinct from surface water.

halite. A common, usually colorless mineral composed of sodium and chlorite that has a distinctive salty taste.

helictite. A curved, twiglike deposit that grows from cave ceilings as water emerging from a nearly microscopic central canal deposits calcium carbonate.

hominid. A member of the biologic family that includes all modern great apes and humans and their extinct ancestors.

host rock. A body of rock serving as a host for other rocks or for mineral deposits.

Iapetus Ocean. An ocean that existed in the general position of the present-day Atlantic Ocean from late Precambrian time to the Devonian Period.

ice sheet. A glacier of considerable thickness covering a large part of a continent.

igneous. A class of rock formed by the crystallization of magma.

index fossil. A fossil that identifies and dates the strata in which it is found.

intrusion. The process by which magma is placed in preexisting rock, and the resulting igneous rock body.

isinglass. Thin, transparent sheets of muscovite mica.

isostasy. The condition of equilibrium in the lithosphere maintained by the yielding of rock in the asthenosphere.

karst. Topography formed on and within carbonate rock that is characterized by caves, sinkholes, and other dissolution features.

kyanite. A blue-green aluminum-rich mineral that occurs in long, thin, blade-shaped crystals.

Laurentia. The late Precambrian to late Paleozoic continent of the northern hemisphere, and counterpart to Gondwanaland in the southern hemisphere, that was the precursor to North America.

lava. Magma that erupts at Earth's surface.

limestone. A sedimentary rock composed principally of calcium carbonate that typically forms in lakes and warm, shallow seas.

lithosphere. The outer layer of Earth in which tectonic plates develop. It is above the asthenosphere and includes the Earth's crust.

mafic. Said of an igneous rock composed of one or more dark-colored ferromagnesian minerals.

magma. Molten or partially molten rock found in the interior of Earth.

mantle. The zone of Earth that lies below the crust and above the core.

massif. A massive topographic and structural feature commonly formed of rock more rigid than those of its surroundings.

mass wasting. A general term for the downslope movement of soil and rock under the influence of gravity.

metamorphic. A class of rock that has changed in appearance due to exposure to high temperatures and pressures within the Earth.

meteorite. A fragment of a celestial body that fell to Earth's surface instead of vaporizing in the atmosphere.

mica. A colored or colorless silica-rich mineral that forms thin, flat sheets.

mineral. A naturally occurring inorganic compound with a characteristic chemical composition resulting in distinctive physical properties, such as color and geometric shape.

monadnock. A rock or hill rising conspicuously above the surrounding landscape.

muscovite. A generally colorless mica mineral commonly found in gneisses and schists.

normal fault. A fault along which rock on one side has moved downward relative to rock on the other side.

opferkessel. A shallow basin formed in silicate rocks and commonly stained by reddish-brown iron minerals.

ore. Naturally occurring rock from which a mineral or minerals of economic value can be extracted.

orogeny. The formation of mountains through tectonic processes.

outcrop. The part of a formation or geologic structure that is exposed at Earth's surface.

Pangaea. The supercontinent that formed late in the Paleozoic Era through the merger of the continents Gondwanaland and Laurentia.

Panthalassa Ocean. The ocean that surrounded the supercontinent Pangaea.

patch reef. A mound-like organic mass frequently forming part of a larger organic mass in a marine setting.

pegmatite. An exceptionally coarse-grained igneous rock that usually occurs as irregular dikes or veins.

pelecypod. A marine or freshwater bivalve with a hinged shell, such as a clam or an oyster.

peneplain. A low, featureless, gently undulating land surface of considerable area produced by erosion over a long time frame.

periglacial. The processes, conditions, climates, and topographic features influenced by the cold temperatures at the margins of glaciers.

phylum. The primary taxonomic division of the animal kingdom.

physiographic province. A region whose pattern of relief features or landforms differs significantly from that of adjacent regions.

Piedmont Province. The physiographic province that extends from southern New York to Alabama and consists of metamorphic and igneous rocks that have been thoroughly weathered to a surface of minimal relief.

plate. A segment of Earth's lithosphere that moves horizontally across the surface and interacts with other independent plates, creating zones of seismic and volcanic activity at their margins.

plate tectonics. The theory that most large features of Earth form through the relative movement and interaction of the rigid plates composing the lithosphere.

pluton. A large igneous intrusion deep beneath Earth's surface.

protocontinent. A landmass that might later become large enough to be considered a major continent.

pyroclastic. Pertaining to clastic rock material formed by volcanic explosion or aerial expulsion from a volcanic vent.

quartzite. A very hard but unmetamorphosed sandstone consisting chiefly of quartz grains that are so solidly cemented together that the rock breaks across, or through, the grains rather than around them.

reptile. Cold-blooded tetrapods that breathe air at all stages of development.

rift. A long, narrow continental trough bounded by normal faults that marks a zone of the lithosphere that is being ruptured by tectonic extension.

ripple mark. An undulatory surface consisting of alternating small-scale ridges and troughs formed on land by wind action and in water by wave action.

Rodinia. The supercontinent that formed toward the end of Precambrian time when ancestral South America, eastern North America, and western Africa merged.

rugose coral. A type of extinct coral that had a wrinkled or ridged surface.

sand. A sedimentary particle ranging in size between 0.0025 and 0.08 inch (0.06 and 2 millimeters) in diameter.

sandstone. A sedimentary rock composed of rounded sand-sized sediment held together by naturally occurring cement.

scale tree. A fossil tree of the Carboniferous Period with an exterior marked by diamond-shaped scars left after leaves fell off the tree.

schist. A strongly foliated, crystalline metamorphic rock that can easily be split into slabs due to the parallel nature of the majority of its minerals.

scolithus. A trace fossil found in quartz-rich sandstones of Paleozoic age consisting of a narrow, straight tube that commonly flares into a cuplike depression at its top.

seam. A particular bed or vein, such as a coal seam, within a series of beds.

sediment. Unconsolidated solid particles that weathered and eroded from rock.

sedimentary. A class of rock formed by the deposition and cementation of sediment.

shield. A speleothem composed of two parallel, hemicircular plates separated by a thin, planar crack.

silt. A sedimentary particle ranging in size between 0.00016 and 0.0025 inch (0.004 and 0.06 millimeter) in diameter.

siltstone. A sedimentary rock composed of silt-sized sediment with a texture that is intermediate between sandstone and shale.

sinkhole. A circular topographic depression in an area of karst.

slate. A dense metamorphic rock that can be split into thin slabs and plates.

spalling. The process by which thin, curved pieces of rock are removed from a rock surface by weathering.

speleothem. Any of the various types of mineral deposits that form in caves.

stalactite. A speleothem that hangs from the ceiling of a cave and develops as calcium carbonate precipitates from water that drips onto the floor.

stalagmite. A speleothem that grows upward from the floor of a cave and develops as minerals precipitate from water that drips onto the floor.

strata. Tabular layers of sedimentary rock separated from each other by a distinctive bedding plane.

stromatolite. An organic sedimentary structure produced by microorganisms that trap sediment as they grow.

supercontinent. A landmass formed by the amalgamation of all existing continents.

suture. A fault that marks the boundary between two plates that were once widely separated.

Taconic Orogeny. The first of three phases of mountain building that were instrumental in the development of the Appalachian Mountains during the Paleozoic Era.

tectonics. Pertaining to the forces involved in the development of the broad architecture of Earth's crust, such as its ocean basins, mountains, folds, and faults.

tektite. A rounded, jet-black body of silicate glass found in groups and generally believed to form when a large hypervelocity meteorite strikes Earth's sediments.

terrain. A region of Earth's surface considered as a physical feature or an ecologic environment.

terrane. A fault-bounded body of rock of regional extent characterized by a geologic history that is different from that of an adjacent terrane.

thrust fault. A fault along which rock on one side has moved upward relative to rock on the other side due to compressive force.

till. A mixture of unconsolidated and unsorted clay, silt, sand, and boulders of different size and shape that was deposited by a glacier.

trilobite. An extinct marine arthropod characterized by a three-lobed exoskeleton.

tuff. Consolidated or cemented volcanic ash.

vein. A mineral deposit that fills a fault or other fracture in rock.

volcanic ash. Fine pyroclastic material that is less than 0.08 inch (2 millimeters) in diameter.

water gap. A deep pass in a mountain ridge through which a stream or river flows.

REFERENCES

1. KIPTOPEKE STATE PARK

Collins, G. S., and K. Wünnemann. 2005. "How Big Was the Chesapeake Bay Impact? Insight from Numerical Modeling." *Geology* 33 (12): 925–928.

Hodge, P. 1994. *Meteorite Craters and Impact Structures of the Earth*. New York: Cambridge University Press.

Koeberl, C., C. W. Poag, W. U. Reimold, and D. Brandt. 1996. "Impact Origin of the Chesapeake Bay Structure and the Source of the North American Tektites." *Science* 271 (5253): 1263–1266.

Poag, C. W. 1998. *The Chesapeake Bay Bolide Impact: A New View of Coastal Plain Evolution*. US Geological Survey Fact Sheet 049-98.

2. LAKE DRUMMOND

Arnold, R. 2012. *The Dismal Swamp and Lake Drummond*. Neuilly-sur-Seine, France: Ulan Press.

Crawford, A. 2015. "The Great Dismal Swamp." *Nature Conservancy* (February/March), 52–59. Available online at https://www.nature.org/magazine/archives/the-great-dismal-swamp.xml.

Simpson, B. 1998. *The Great Dismal: A Carolinian's Swamp Memoir*. Chapel Hill, NC: University of North Carolina Press.

Wetzel, R. G. 2001. *Limnology: Lake and River Ecosystems*. 3rd ed. San Diego, CA: Academic Press.

3. VIRGINIA LIVING MUSEUM

Fastovsky, D. E., and D. B. Weishampel. 2016. *Dinosaurs: A Concise Natural History*. 3rd ed. New York: Cambridge University Press.

Hughes, C. D. 2011. *National Geographic Little Kids First Big Book of Dinosaurs*. Washington, DC: National Geographic.

Naish, D., and P. M. Barrett. 2016. *Dinosaurs: How They Lived and Evolved*. Washington, DC: Smithsonian Books.

Stine, M. 2017. *What Was the Age of the Dinosaurs?* New York: Grosset and Dunlap.

4. CHIPPOKES PLANTATION STATE PARK

Campbell, L. D. 1993. *Pliocene Molluscs from the Yorktown and Chowan River Formations in Virginia*. Virginia Division of Mineral Resources Publication 127.

Say, T. 1824. "An Account of Some of the Fossil Shells of Maryland." In *Journal of the Academy of Natural Sciences of Philadelphia*, vol. 4, pt. 1, 124–155. Philadelphia: J. Harding.

Ward, L. W., and B. W. Blackwelder. 1975. Chesapecten, *a new genus of Pectinidae (Mullusca: Bivalvia) from the Miocene and Pliocene of Eastern North America*. US Geological Survey Professional Paper 861.

5. YORK RIVER STATE PARK

Beatty, B. L., and A. C. Dooley, Jr. 2013. "The First Terrestrial Mammal from the Late Miocene Eastover Formation of Virginia." *Jeffersoniana* 29: 1–6.

Hobbs, C. H., III. 2004. "Geological History of Chesapeake Bay, USA." *Quaternary Science Reviews* 23 (5–6): 641–661.

Toscano, M. A., and L. L. York. 1992. "Quaternary Stratigraphy and Sea-Level History of the U.S. Middle Atlantic Coastal Plain." *Quaternary Science Reviews* 11 (3): 301–328.

Ward, L. W., and B. W. Blackwelder. 1980. *Stratigraphic Revision of Upper Miocene and Lower Pliocene Beds of the Chesapeake Group, Middle Atlantic Coastal Plain.* US Geological Survey Bulletin 1482-D.

6. GREAT FALLS OF THE POTOMAC

Dietrich, R. V. 1990. *Geology and Virginia.* Charlottesville, VA: Virginia Division of Mineral Resources.

Frye, K. 1990. *Roadside Geology of Virginia.* Missoula, MT: Mountain Press Publishing.

Reed, J. C., Jr., R. S. Sigafoos, and G. W. Fisher. 1980. *The River and the Rocks: The Geologic Story of Great Falls and the Potomac River Gorge.* US Geological Survey Bulletin 1471.

7. LAKE ANNA STATE PARK

Linden, M. A., J. R. Craig, and T. N. Solberg. 1985. "Mineralogy and Chemistry of Gold in the Virginia District, Halifax County, Virginia." *Virginia Minerals* 31 (2): 17–22.

Pardee, J. T., and C. F. Park Jr. 1948. *Gold Deposits of the Southern Piedmont.* US Geological Survey Professional Paper 213.

Spears, D. B., and M. L. Upchurch. 1997. *Metallic Mines, Prospects and Occurrences in the Gold-Pyrite Belt of Virginia.* Virginia Division of Mineral Resources Publication 147.

Sweet, P. C. 2003. *Gold in Virginia.* Virginia Division of Mineral Resources Publication 19.

8. BUZZARD MOUNTAIN

Lee, K. Y. 1980. *Triassic-Jurassic Geology of the Southern Part of the Culpeper Basin and the Barboursville Basin, Virginia.* US Geological Survey Open-File Report 80-468.

Nield, T. 2009. *Supercontinent: Ten Billion Years in the Life of Our Planet.* Cambridge, MA: Harvard University Press.

Roberts, J. K. 1928. *The Geology of the Virginia Triassic.* Virginia Geological Survey Bulletin 29.

Spencer, E. W. 2017. *Guide to the Geology and Natural History of the Blue Ridge Mountains.* United States: Edgar W. Spencer.

9. POTHOLES ON BELLE ISLE

Darton, N. H. 1911. *Economic Geology of Richmond, Virginia, and Vicinity.* US Geological Survey Bulletin 483.

Dietrich, R. V. 1990. *Geology and Virginia.* Charlottesville, VA: University of Virginia Press.

Frye, K. 1990. *Roadside Geology of Virginia.* Missoula, MT: Mountain Press Publishing.

Goodwin, B. K. 1978. "Potholes." *Virginia Minerals* 24 (4): 36–37.

10. QUARRY GARDENS

Burfoot, J. D., Jr., 1930. "The Origin of the Talc and Soapstone Deposits of Virginia." *Economic Geology* 25 (8): 805–826.

Groff, G. G. 1991. *Soapstone Shortlines: Alberene Stone and its Railroads.* Charlottesville, VA: Drop Leaf Press.

Hess, H. H. 1933. "Hydrothermal Metamorphism of an Ultrabasic Intrusive at Schuyler, Virginia." *American Journal of Science* 26 (154): 377–408.

Smith, J. W. 1961. "Talc, Soapstone and Related Stone Deposits of Virginia." *Virginia Minerals* 7 (2): 1–8.

11. WILLIS MOUNTAIN

Dixon, G. B., Jr. 1980. "Kyanite Mining in Virginia." *Virginia Minerals* 26 (1): 12.

Frye, K. 1990. *Roadside Geology of Virginia*. Missoula, MT: Mountain Press Publishing.

Owens, B. E., and M. A. Pasek. 2007. "Kyanite Quartzites in the Piedmont Province of Virginia: Evidence for a Possible High-Sulfidation System." *Economic Geology* 102 (3): 495–509.

Virginia Division of Mineral Resources. 1981. *Geologic Investigations in the Willis Mountain and Andersonville Quadrangles, Virginia*. Virginia Division of Mineral Resources Publication 29.

12. AMELIA PEGMATITES

Glass, J. J. 1935. "The Pegmatite Minerals from Near Amelia, Virginia." *American Mineralogist* 20: 741–768.

Kearns, L. E., and B. S. Martin. 2000. "The Morefield Pegmatite, Amelia, Virginia: Mineral Update." *Virginia Minerals* 46 (2): 9–13.

Pegau, A. A. 1932. *Pegmatite Deposits of Virginia*. Virginia Geological Survey Bulletin 33. Richmond, VA: Division of Purchase and Printing.

Sinkankas, J. 1968. "Classic Mineral Occurrences: I. Geology and Mineralogy of the Rutherford Pegmatites, Amelia, Virginia." *American Mineralogist* 53 (March-April): 373–405.

13. NOTTOWAY FALLS

Lerner, K. L., and B. W. Lerner 2003. *World of Earth Science*. Detroit, MI: Thomson-Gale.

Simonds, M. H. K., K. E. Lang, C. M Bailey, C. P. Abbott, and W. P. Kirkwood. 2017. "Kinematic History of Granitic Gneisses at the Falls of the Nottoway in the Carolina Terrane, Eastern Piedmont, Virginia." *Geologic Society of America Abstracts with Programs* 49 (3).

Tarbuck, E. J., and F. K. Lutgens. 1997. *Earth Science*. 8th ed. Upper Saddle River, NJ: Prentice Hall.

14. TRIASSIC BASINS OF THE PIEDMONT

Henika, W. S. 1977. *Geology of the Blairs, Mount Hermon, Danville and Ringgold Quadrangles, Virginia*. Virginia Division of Mineral Resources Publication 2.

Meyertons, C. T. 1963. *Triassic Formations of the Danville Basin*. Virginia Division of Mineral Resources Report of Investigations 6.

Olsen, P. E., D. L. Daniels, J. W. Gore, A. J. Froelich, and J. P. Smooth. 1991. "Rift Basins of Early Mesozoic Age." In *The Geology of the Carolinas*, edited by J. W. Horton Jr. and V. A. Zullo, 142–170. Knoxville, TN: University of Tennessee Press.

15. VIRGINIA MUSEUM OF NATURAL HISTORY

Holtz, T. R. 2015. *T. Rex: Hunter or Scavenger*. New York: Random House Children's Books.

Leis, R. J., and B. L. Stinchcomb. 2015. *Stromatolites: Ancient, Beautiful, and Earth-Altering*. Atglen, PA: Schiffer Publishing.

Thewissen, J. G. M. 2014. *The Walking Whales: From Land to Water in Eight Million Years*. Oakland, CA: University of California Press.

16. FAIRY STONE STATE PARK

Deer, W. A., R. A. Howie, and J. Zussman. 1996. *An Introduction to the Rock-Forming Minerals*. 2nd ed. London: Pearson Publishers.

Simmons, R. 2009. *Stones of the New Consciousness: Healing, Awakening and Co-Creating with Crystals, Minerals, and Gems*. Berkeley, CA: North Atlantic Books.

Walters, R. J. L. 1996. *The Power of Gemstones*. London: Carlton Books.

17. FANCY GAP INCLINE

Badger, R. L. 1999. *Geology along Skyline Drive: Shenandoah National Park, Virginia*. Guilford, CT: Falcon Press.

Dietrich, R. V. 1990. *Geology and Virginia*. Charlottesville, VA: University of Virginia Press.

Frye, K. 1990. *Roadside Geology of Virginia*. Missoula, MT: Mountain Press Publishing.

18. MOUNT ROGERS

Bennett, M. M., and N. F. Glasser (eds.). 2009. *Glacial Geology: Ice Sheets and Landforms*. 2nd ed. Hoboken, NJ: Wiley-Blackwell.

Rankin, D. W. 1993. *The Volcanogenic Mount Rogers Formation and the Overlying Glaciogenic Konnarock Formation: Two Late Proterozoic Units in Southwestern Virginia*. US Geological Survey Bulletin 2029.

Silverstein, A., V. B. Silverstein, and L. Silverstein Nunn. 2009. *Volcanoes: The Science Behind Fiery Eruptions*. New York: Enslow.

Tollo, R. P., M. J. Bartholomew, J. P. Hibbard, and P. M. Karabinos (eds.). 2010. *From Rodinia to Pangea: the Lithotectonic Record of the Appalachian Region*. Geological Society of America Memoirs 206. Boulder, CO: Geological Society of America.

19. GOSSAN "LEAD" DISTRICT

Currier, L. W. 1935. *Zinc and Lead Region of Southwestern Virginia*. Virginia Division of Mineral Resources Bulletin 43.

Gair, J. E., and J. F. Slack 1984. "Deformation, Geochemistry and Origin of Massive Sulfide Deposits, Gossan Lead District, Virginia." *Economic Geology* 79 (7): 1483–1520.

Kline, M. H., and T. J. Ballard 1949. *Investigation of the Great Gossan Lead, Carroll County, Virginia*. US Bureau of Mines Report of Investigations 4532.

Wright, R. J., and N. D. Raman. 1948. *The Gossan Lead, Carroll County, Virginia*. US Geological Survey Open-File Report 48-3.

Young, R. S. 1956. "Sulfides in Virginia." *Virginia Minerals* 2 (1): 1–7.

20. DEVIL'S MARBLEYARD

French, H. M. 2017. *The Periglacial Environment*. 4th ed. Hoboken, NJ: Wiley-Blackwell.

Goodwin, P. W., and E. J. Anderson 1974. "Associated Physical and Biogenic Structures in Environmental Subdivision of a Cambrian Tidal Sand Body." *Journal of Geology* 82 (6): 779–794.

King, P. B. 1950. *Geology of the Elkton Area, Virginia*. US Geological Survey Professional Paper 230.

Schwab, F. L. 1970. "Origin of the Antietam Formation (Late Precambrian? Lower Cambrian), Central Virginia." *Journal of Sedimentary Research* 40 (1): 354–366.

21. CRABTREE FALLS

Bloomer, R. O., and H. J. Werner 1955. "Geology of the Blue Ridge Region in Central Virginia." *Geological Society of America Bulletin* 66 (5): 579–606.

Dietrich, R. V. 1990. *Geology and Virginia*. Charlottesville, VA: University of Virginia Press.

Gathright, T. M., II. 1976. *Geology of the Shenandoah National Park, Virginia*. Virginia Division of Mineral Resources Bulletin 86.

Tollo, R. P., J. N. Aleinikoff, E. A. Borduas, P. C. Hackley, and C. M. Fanning. 2004. "Petrologic and Geochronologic Evolution of the Grenville Orogeny, Northern Blue Ridge Province, Virginia." In *Proterozoic Tectonic Evolution of the Grenville Orogen in North America*, Geological Society of America Memoir 197, edited by R. P. Tollo, J. McLelland, L. Corriveau, and M. J. Bartholomew, 647–678. Boulder, CO: Geological Society of America.

22. HUMPBACK ROCKS

Badger, R. L., 1999. *Geology along Skyline Drive: Shenandoah National Park, Virginia*. Guilford, CT: Falcon Press.

Bartholomew, M. J. 1977. *Geology of the Greenfield and Sherando Quadrangles, Virginia*. Virginia Division of Mineral Resources Publication 4.

Bloomer, R. O., and R. R. Bloomer. 1947. "The Catoctin Formation in Central Virginia." *Journal of Geology* 55 (2): 94–106.

Reed, J. C., Jr. 1969. *Ancient Lavas in Shenandoah National Park, Near Luray, Virginia*. US Geological Survey Bulletin 1265.

23. OLD RAG MOUNTAIN

Bashore, H. W. 2006. *Old Rag Mountain: Rebirth of a Wilderness*. Charlottesville, VA: University of Virginia Press.

Crandall, H., and R. Engle. 1997. *Shenandoah: The Story Behind the Scenery*. Las Vegas, NV: KC Publications.

Gathright, T. M., II. 1976. *Geology of the Shenandoah National Park, Virginia*. Virginia Division of Mineral Resources Bulletin 86.

Heatwole, H. 1988. *Guide to Shenandoah National Park (Formerly Guide to "Skyline Drive")*. Bulletin 9. Luray, VA: Shenandoah Natural History Association.

24. MARYS ROCK

Badger, R. L. 1999. *Geology along Skyline Drive: Shenandoah National Park, Virginia*. Guilford, CT: Falcon Press.

Gathright, T. M., II. 1976. *Geology of the Shenandoah National Park, Virginia*. Virginia Division of Mineral Resources Bulletin 86.

Reed, J. C., Jr., 1969. *Ancient Lavas in Shenandoah National Park, Near Luray, Virginia*. US Geological Survey Bulletin 1265.

Wickham, J. S. 1972. "Structural History of a Portion of the Blue Ridge, Northern Virginia." *Geological Society of America Bulletin* 83 (3): 723–760.

25. COMPTON PEAK

Badger, R. L. 1999. *Geology along Skyline Drive: Shenandoah National Park, Virginia*. Guilford, CT: Falcon Press.

Bailey, C. M., S. Southworth, and R. P. Tollo. 2006. "Tectonic History of the Blue Ridge, North-Central Virginia." In *Excursions in Geology and History: Field Trips in the Middle Atlantic States*, Field Guide 8, edited by F. J. Pazzaglia, 113–134. Boulder, CO: Geological Society of America.

Gathright, T. M., II. 1976. *Geology of the Shenandoah National Park, Virginia*. Virginia Division of Mineral Resources Bulletin 86.

Reed, J. C., Jr. 1969. *Ancient Lavas in Shenandoah National Park, Near Luray, Virginia*. US Geological Survey Bulletin 1265.

26. PASSAGE CREEK

Hupp, C. R. 1983. "Geo-Botanical Evidence of Late Quaternary Mass Wasting in Block Field Areas of Virginia." *Earth Surface Processes and Landforms* 8 (5): 439–450.

Hupp, C. R., and W. R. Osterkamp. 1985. "Bottomland Vegetation Distribution along Passage Creek, Virginia, in Relation to Fluvial Landforms." *Ecology* 66 (3): 670–681.

Hupp, C. R., and R. S. Sigafoos. 1982. "Plant Growth and Block-Field Movement in Virginia." In *Sediment Budgets and Routing in Forested Drainage Basins*, US Forest Service General Technical Report PNW-141, edited by F. L. Swanson, R. J. Janda, T. Dunne, and D. N. Swanston, 78–85.

Rader, E. K., and T. H. Biggs. 1976. *Geology of the Strasburg and Toms Brook Quadrangles, Virginia*. Virginia Division of Mineral Resources Report of Investigations 45.

27. CHIMNEY ROCK

Brent, W. B. 1960. *Geology and Mineral Resources of Rockingham County*. Virginia Division of Mineral Resources Bulletin 76.

Johnson, M. R. W., and S. L. Harley. 2012. *Orogenesis: The Making of Mountains*. New York: Cambridge University Press.

Rader, E. K., and W. J. Perry. 1976. "Reinterpretation of the Geology of Brocks Gap, Rockingham County, Virginia." *Virginia Minerals* 22 (4): 37–45.

28. ENDLESS CAVERNS

Bogli, A. 1980. *Karst Hydrology and Physical Speleology*. New York: Springer-Verlag.

Bretz, J. H. 1942. "Vadose and Phreatic Features of Limestone Caverns." *Journal of Geology* 50 (6): 675–811.

Davis, W. M. 1930. "Origin of Limestone Caverns." *Geological Society of America Bulletin* 41 (3): 475–628.

Edwards, I. 1927. "Underground Geology at the Endless Caverns, New Market, Virginia." In *Milwaukee Public Museum Yearbook*, vol. 5, p. 82–104.

29. MOLE HILL

Brent, W. B. 1960. *Geology and Mineral Resources of Rockingham County*. Virginia Division of Mineral Resources Bulletin 76.

Butts, C. 1940. *Geology of the Appalachian Valley in Virginia*. Virginia Division of Mineral Resources Bulletin 52.

Johnson, R. W., Jr., C. Milton, and J. M. Dennison. 1971. *Field Trip to the Igneous Rocks of Augusta, Rockingham, Highland, and Bath Counties*. Virginia Division of Mineral Resources Information Circular 16.

Tso, J. L., and J. D. Surber. 2002. "Eocene Igneous Rocks near Monterey, Virginia: A Field Study." *Virginia Minerals* 48: 25–40.

30. NATURAL CHIMNEYS PARK

Edmundson, R. S. 1958. *Industrial Limestones and Dolomites in Virginia: James River District, West of the Blue Ridge*. Virginia Division of Mineral Resources Bulletin 73.

Dietrich, R. V. 1990. *Geology and Virginia*. Charlottesville, VA: University of Virginia Press.

Noel, J. P., and B. Jones. 2015. *Origin of Carbonate Sedimentary Rocks*. New York: John Wiley and Sons.

31. GRAND CAVERNS

Halliday, W. R. (ed.). 1968. "The Grottoes of the Shenandoah." *Journal of Spelean History* 1 (2): 1–26.

Palmer, A. N. 2007. *Cave Geology*. Cave City, KY: Cave Books.

Taylor, M. R., and R. C. Kerbo. 2001. *Caves: Exploring Hidden Realms*. Washington, DC: National Geographic Society.

Waltham, T. 2008. *Great Caves of the World*. Richmond Hill, ON: Firefly Books.

32. EAGLE ROCK

Bartholomew, M. J., A. P. Schultz, W. S. Henika, and T. M. Gathright II. 1982. "Geology of the Blue Ridge and Valley and Ridge at the Junction of the Central and Southern Appalachians. " In *Central Appalachian Geology*, edited by P. T. Lyttle, 121–170. American Geological Institute.

Bick, K. F. 1973. "Complexities of Overthrust Faults in Central Virginia." *American Journal of Science*, Cooper Volume 273-A: 343–352.

McGuire, O. S. 1970. *Geology of the Eagle Rock, Strom, Oriskany, and Salisbury Quadrangles, Virginia*. Virginia Division of Mineral Resources Report of Investigations 24.

33. MOUNT HOREB KIMBERLITE

Dietrich, R. V. 1990. *Minerals of Virginia*. Charlottesville, VA: Virginia Division of Mineral Resources.

Pasteris, J. D. 1983. "Kimberlites: A Look into the Earth's Mantle." *American Scientist* 71 (3): 282–288.

Sears, C. E., and M. C. Gilbert. 1973. "Petrography of the Mount Horeb Kimberlite." *Geological Society of America Abstracts* 5 (5): 434.

Sweet, P. C. 1996. "Diamonds in Virginia." *Virginia Minerals* 42 (4): 33–40.

34. NATURAL BRIDGE STATE PARK

Catlin, D. T. 1984. *A Naturalist's Blue Ridge Parkway*. Knoxville, TN: University of Tennessee Press.

Frye, K. 1990. *Roadside Geology of Virginia*. Missoula, MT: Mountain Press Publishing.

Spencer, E. W. 1968. *Geology of the Natural Bridge, Sugarloaf Mountain, Buchanan, and Arnold Valley Quadrangles, Virginia*. Virginia Division of Mineral Resources Report of Investigations 13.

Spencer, E. W. 1985. *Guidebook to the Natural Bridge and Natural Bridge Caverns*. Lexington, VA: Poorhouse Mountain Studios.

35. MCAFEE KNOB

Bailey, C. M., W. C. Sherwood, L. S. Eaton, and D. S. Powars. 2016. *The Geology of Virginia*. Martinsville, VA: Virginia Museum of Natural History.

Burnham, B., and M. Burnham. 2013. *Hiking Virginia*. Guilford, CT: Falcon Press.

Whisonant, R. C. 1977. "Nature of Porosity in Tuscarora Sandstone (Lower Silurian) in the Appalachian Basin." *Oil and Gas Journal* 88: 215–220.

Woodward, H. P. 1932. *Geology and Mineral Resources of the Roanoke Area, Virginia*. Virginia Geological Survey Bulletin 34.

36. SINKING CREEK MOUNTAIN

Schultz, A. P. 1986. "Ancient, Giant Rockslides, Sinking Creek Mountain, Southern Appalachians, Virginia." *Geology* 14 (1): 11–14.

Schultz, A. P., and C. S. Southworth (eds.). 1987. *Landslides of Eastern North America*. United States Geological Survey Circular 1008.

Schultz, A. P., and C. S. Southworth. 1989. "Large Bedrock Landslides of the Appalachian Valley and Ridge Province of Eastern North America." In *Landslide Process of the Eastern United States and Puerto Rico*, GSA Special Papers, vol. 236, edited by A. P. Schultz and R. W. Johnson, 57–74. Boulder, CO: Geological Society of America.

Southworth, C. S., and A. P. Schultz. 1986. *Characteristics of Giant Rockslides in the Appalachian Valley and Ridge, Virginia, West Virginia, Maryland, and Pennsylvania*. United States Geological Survey Open-File Report 86-94.

37. DIXIE CAVERNS

Hack, J. T. 1977. *Geology of Luray Caverns, Virginia*. Virginia Division of Mineral Resources Report of Investigations 3.

Halliday, W. R. 1966. *Depths of the Earth: Caves and Caverns of the United States*. New York: Joanna Cotler Books.

Taylor, M. R., and R. C. Kerbo. 2001. *Caves: Exploring Hidden Realms*. Washington, DC: National Geographic Society.

38. MOUNTAIN LAKE

Darlington, W. M. 1893. *Christopher Gist's Journals, with Historical, Geographical and Ethnological Notes and Biographies of his Contemporaries*. Pittsburgh, PA: J. R. Weldin and Company.

Mills, H. H. 1988. *Surficial Geology and Geomorphology of the Mountain Lake Area, Giles County, Virginia, Including Sedimentological Studies of Colluvium and Boulder Streams*. US Geological Survey Professional Paper 1469.

Parker, B. C., H. E. Wolfe, and R. V. Howard. 1975. "On the Origin and History of Mountain Lake, Virginia." *Southeastern Geology* 16 (4): 213–226.

Sharp, H. S. 1933. "The Origin of Mountain Lake, Virginia." *Journal of Geology* 41 (6): 636–641.

39. COAL MINING HERITAGE PARK

Bird, S. O. 1997. *Virginia's Coal Ages*. Virginia Division of Mineral Resources Publication 149.

Campbell, M. R., and F. C. Pederson. 1925. *The Valley Coal Fields of Virginia*. Virginia Geological Survey Bulletin 25.

La Lone, M. B. 1997. *Appalachian Coal Mining Memories: Life in the Coal Fields of Virginia's New River Valley*. Blacksburg, VA: Pocahontas Press.

Whisonant, R. C. 2000. "Geology and History of the Confederate Coal Mines in Montgomery County, Virginia." *Virginia Minerals* 46 (1): 1–7.

40. NARROWS WATER GAP

Adams, N. 2002. *Far Appalachia: Following the New River North*. New York: Dell Publishing.

Clark, G. M. 1989. "Central and Southern Appalachian Water and Wind Gap Origins: Review and New Data." *Geomorphology* 2 (1–3): 209–232.

Fryirs, K. A., and G. J. Brierley. 2012. *Geomorphic Analysis of River Systems: An Approach to Reading the Landscape*. West Sussex, UK: Wiley-Blackwell.

Small, R. J. 1978. *The Study of Landforms: A Textbook of Geomorphology*. London: Cambridge University Press.

41. RADFORD UNIVERSITY MUSEUM OF THE EARTH SCIENCES

Hess, H., W. I. Ausich, C. E. Brett, and M. J. Simms. 1999. *Fossil Crinoids*. Cambridge, UK: Cambridge University Press.

Levi-Setti, R. 2014. *The Trilobite Book: A Visual Journey*. Chicago: University of Chicago Press.

Schneider, S. 2011. *Collecting Fluorescent Minerals*. Atglen, PA: Schiffer Publishing.

Switek, B., and J. Csotonyi. 2016. *The T. Rex Handbook*. Kennebunkport, ME: Applesauce Press.

42. BURKES GARDEN

Barranger, H. 1993. "The Majesty of Burkes Garden—The Beauty of Tazewell County." *Blue Ridge Country Magazine* 6 (3):43–49.

Cooper, B. N. 1944. *The Geology and Mineral Resources of the Burkes Garden Quadrangle, Virginia*. Virginia Geological Survey Bulletin 60.

Dietrich, R. V. 1990. *Geology and Virginia*. Charlottesville, VA: University of Virginia Press.

Frye, K. 1990. *Roadside Geology of Virginia*. Missoula, MT: Mountain Press Publishing.

43. MUSEUM OF THE MIDDLE APPALACHIANS

Kent, W. B. 1955. *A History of Saltville, Virginia*. Radford, VA: Commonwealth Press.

Kurlansky, M. 2003. *Salt: A World History*. New York: Penguin Books.

Ray, C. E., B. N. Cooper, and W. S. Benninghoff. 1967. "Fossil Mammals and Pollen in a Late Pleistocene Deposit at Saltville, Virginia." *Journal of Paleontology* 41 (3): 608–622.

Whisonant, R. C. 1996. "Geology and the Civil War in Southwestern Virginia: The Smyth County Salt Works." *Virginia Minerals* 42 (3): 21–30.

44. GREAT CHANNELS

Dietrich, R. V. 1990. *Geology and Virginia*. Charlottesville, VA: University of Virginia Press.

Frye, K. 1990. *Roadside Geology of Virginia*. Missoula, MT: Mountain Press Publishing.

Taillant, J. D. 2015. *Glaciers: The Politics of Ice*. New York: Oxford University Press.

Weidensaul, S. 2016. *Mountains of the Heart: A Natural History of the Appalachians*. Golden, CO: Fulcrum Publishing.

45. SINKHOLE VALLEY

Friend, S. 2002. *Sinkholes*. Sarasota, FL: Pineapple Press.

Hubbard, D. A. 2001. *Selected Karst Features of the Southern Valley and Ridge Province, Virginia*. Virginia Division of Mineral Resources Publication 167.

Waltham, T., F. Bell, M. Culshaw, M. Knez, and T. Slabe. 2005. *Sinkholes and Subsidence: Karst and Cavernous Rocks in Engineering and Construction*. New York: Springer.

White, W. B. (ed.). 2015. *The Caves of Burnsville Cove, Virginia: Fifty Years of Exploration and Science*. New York: Springer.

46. NATURAL TUNNEL STATE PARK

Fugate, C. T. 1986. *The Legend of Natural Tunnel*. Blacksburg, VA: Pocahontas Press.

Milici, R. C. 1990. "The Geology of Natural Tunnel State Park." *Virginia Minerals* 36 (3): 17–26.

Scales, T. 2004. *Natural Tunnel: Nature's Marvel in Stone*. Johnson City, TN: Overmountain Press.

Woodward, H. P. 1936. "Natural Bridge and Natural Tunnel, Virginia." *Journal of Geology* 44 (5): 604–616.

47. MILLBRIG ASHFALL

Frye, K. 1990. *Roadside Geology of Virginia*. Missoula, MT: Mountain Press Publishing.

Huff, W. D., S. M. Bergström, and D. R. Kolata. 1992. "Gigantic Ordovician Volcanic Ash Fall in North America and Europe: Biological, Tectonomagmatic, and Event-Stratigraphic Significance." *Geology* 20 (10): 875–878.

Huffman, G. G. 1945. "Middle Ordovician Limestones from Lee County, Virginia, to Central Kentucky." *Journal of Geology* 53 (3): 145–174.

Kolata, D. R., W. D. Huff, and S. M. Bergström. 1996. *Ordovician K-Bentonite of Eastern North America*. GSA Special Paper 313. Boulder, CO: Geological Society of America.

48. CUMBERLAND GAP

Dietz, R. S. 1966. "Shatter Cones at the Middlesboro Structure, Kentucky." *Meteoritics* 3 (1): 27–79.

Kortenkamp, S. 2004. "Impact at Cumberland Gap: Where Natural and National History Collide." *Planetary Science Institute Newsletter* 5 (2): 1–2.

Moshier, S. O., and C. S. Dean (eds.). 1989. *Cumberland Mountain: The Inside Story*. Guidebook for 1987 Field Conference. Kentucky Geological Survey Series 11.

Wiley, M. E. 2014. *Cumberland Gap National Historical Park*. Mount Pleasant, SC: Arcadia Publishing.

49. POCAHONTAS MINE

Bird, S. O. 1997. *Virginia's Coal Ages*. Virginia Division of Mineral Resources Publication 149.

Jones, J. M. 1983. *Early Coal Mining in Pocahontas, Virginia, with Illustrations*. Lynchburg, VA: Jack M. Jones Publishing.

Yarrow, M., and R. Yarrow. 2015. *Voices from the Appalachian Coalfields: Found Poems*. Huron, OH: Bottom Dog Press.

50. BREAKS INTERSTATE PARK

Dietrich, R. V. 1990. *Geology and Virginia*. Charlottesville, VA: University of Virginia Press.

Greb, S. F., W. M. Andrews, and R. A. Smith. 2006. *Geology and Geomorphology of the Breaks Interstate Park Area*. Lexington, KY: Kentucky Geological Survey.

Miller, R. L. 1973. "Where and Why of Pine Mountain and Other Major Fault Planes, Virginia, Kentucky and Tennessee." *American Journal of Science* 273A: 353–371.

Scales, T. 2011. *The Breaks: The Grand Canyon of the South*. Johnson City, TN: Overmountain Press.

INDEX

Rappahannock River, 13
red beds, 42–43
reptiles, 8, 10, 18
rhyolite, 52, 53
rhythmite, 52, 53
Richmond, 7, 10, 14, 22, 26, 32
Richmond Basin, 10, 43
Ridgeley Sandstone, 72, 73
rifts, 9, 10, 30
ripple marks, 88, 106, 109
Roanoke, 5, 44, 58
Roanoke County, 88, 92
Rockbridge County, 56, 84
Rockingham County, 28, 72, 74, 76
Rock of Ages quarry, 100
Rocky Face Fault, 114
Rodinia, x, 2, 3, 6, 8, 50, 52, 58, 61, 62, 64, 66, 67
Rogers, Mount, 48, 49, 52, 53
Roman cross, 46, 47
Round Mountain, 102
rugose coral, 6
Russell County, 108
Russell Fork, 120, 121, 122
Russell Fork Fault, 120, 122
Rutherford Mine, 38, 39
rutile, 36, 38, 62

salt, 16, 94, 104, 105
Saltville, 5, 104, 105
sandstone, 4, 6, 10, 42, 56, 83, 91, 94, 102, 106. See also Bee Rock Sandstone; Clinch Quartzite; Massanutten Sandstone; Ridgeley Sandstone; Tuscarora Sandstone
Say, Thomas, 20
scale trees, 8
scallops, 20, 22
schist, 25, 28, 42, 43, 46, 47, 50, 51
Schuyler, 34
scolithus, 56, 57, 89
Scott County, 110
Scottsville Basin, 43
Scyphocrinites, 100
sea lilies, 100
semianthracite, 96
sharks, 5, 20, 45
shatter cones, 114, 115
Shenandoah County, 70

Shenandoah National Park, 49, 62, 64, 67
Shenandoah Valley, 5, 61, 69, 74, 80
shields, 74, 80, 81
shocked quartz, 14, 16, 94, 114
Siberian Traps, 60
siltstone, 42
Silurian Period, x, 5, 6, 7, 70, 88, 91, 94. See also Clinch Quartzite
Sinkhole Valley, 108–109
sinkholes, 74, 86, 92, 108
Sinking Creek Mountain, 90–91
Skyline Drive, 49, 64, 65, 66
slate, 25, 28
slot canyons, 106, 107
Smyth County, 52, 104
snails, 4, 22, 23, 72, 102
snowball Earth, 53
soapstone, 34–35
spalling, 73
spessartite, 38
spheroidal weathering, 62, 63
Spinosaurus, 18
Spotsylvania County, 28
St. Andrews crosses, 46, 47
stalactites, 5, 69, 74, 75, 80, 92, 93
stalagmites, 5, 69, 74, 75, 81, 93
Stateline Overlook, 120, 121, 122
staurolite, 46–47
steatite, 34
stromatolites, 44, 45
subbituminous, 8, 117
sulfide, 28, 54
supercontinents, 2, 3, 8. See also Pangaea; Rodinia
Surry County, 20

T. rex, 45, 101
Taconic Mountains, 4, 5, 6
Taconic Orogeny, x, 4, 5, 8, 28, 36
talc, 34, 36
Taylorsville Basin, 43
Tazewell County, 102, 117
tectonics, 1, 2, 82, 110
teeth, 10, 20, 100, 101, 104
tektite, 14
Tenontosaurus, 18
Terataspis, 100, 101
terrane, 4, 8, 25, 36
Tethys Ocean, 8

tetrapods, 7
Theodore Roosevelt Island, 27
Tidewater region, 13
Tippecanoe Basin, 5
Tippecanoe Sea, 5, 6
Towers, the, 120, 121, 122
trace fossil, 56, 88, 102, 106
tracks, 18, 113
Triassic Period, x, 9, 10, 30, 42, 43, 96
Triassic Basins, x, 42–43
triceratops, 18
trilobites, 4, 6, 7, 9, 45, 100, 102, 110
Trimble Knob, 76
Turritella, 22, 23
Tuscarora Sandstone, 88, 89
Twin Mountain, 30
twinned crystals, 46–47
Tye River, 58
tyrannosaurus, 18, 45, 100
Tyrannosaurus rex, 100

uranium, 25, 40

Vaalbara, 2
Valley and Ridge, 5, 6, 10, 32, 49, 69, 72, 80, 88, 102
veins, 28, 30, 38, 40, 41, 54, 96
velociraptors, 18
Victoria, 40
Virginia Living Museum, 18–19, 23, 39
Virginia Museum of Natural History, 44–45
Virginia Seismic Zone, 10
volcanic ash, 28, 112
volcanoes, 76, 113
Vulcans Forge, 78

Washington Count, 52, 106
Washington DC, 26
water gaps, 68, 98, 99, 114
Watergate Complex, 27
weathering, 30, 50, 67; differential, 69; freeze-thaw, 10, 56, 57, 70, 106; spalling, 73; spheroidal, 62, 63
whales, 22, 44
Whitetop Mountain, 52
Willis Mountain, 24, 36–37
Winchester, 5, 6, 68
worm burrows, 56, 88, 106

York River State Park, 22–23

ABOUT THE AUTHOR

Born in Ohio, Albert Binkley Dickas earned BA and MA degrees from Miami University, in Oxford, Ohio. After serving with the US Navy Hydrographic Office in Washington, DC, he completed a PhD in petroleum geology at Michigan State University, followed by three years as a development geologist with Magnolia Petroleum (Mobil Oil) in the Gulf of Mexico salt dome province of Louisiana. Another four years were spent as an exploration geologist with Standard Oil of California, where he specialized in the search for hydrocarbon reserves in the Submarine Canyon province of the Sacramento Valley. Having satisfied his strong belief that firsthand industrial experience is a prerequisite for an effective career in higher education, he joined the faculty of the University of Wisconsin–Superior. Over the course of thirty-one years in academia he taught a range of classroom, field, and laboratory courses; founded an environmental research center with a focus on the Lake Superior Basin; established a cooperative research and teaching program with Rostov State University (Russia); and retired as vice chancellor for research. He formed numerous field conferences, authored or coauthored more than sixty published papers, coedited three books, and delivered presentations (as far afield as Nova Scotia, Japan, and Siberia) on the subject of worldwide Precambrian rift structures and their association with Precambrian-age hydrocarbon reservoirs. Today he lives on the crest of Brush Mountain in southwest Virginia, where he continues to write and plan travel excursions in the quest for new and interesting geological sites on all seven continents. He is the author of *101 American Geo-Sites You've Gotta See* (2012), *Ohio Rocks!* (2015), and *101 American Fossil Sites You've Gotta See* (2018), all published by Mountain Press Publishing Company.